MERLIN

THE STORY OF A WESTCOUNTRY LEOPARD
– *A True Tale of Our Times* –

written and illustrated by
TREVOR BEER

ryelands

Originally published by Halsgrove, 2008

Copyright © 2008 Trevor Beer

British Library Cataloguing-in-Publication Data
A CIP record for this title is available from the British Library

ISBN 978 1 906551 01 8

RYELANDS
Halsgrove House
Ryelands Industrial Estate
Bagley Road, Wellington, Somerset TA21 9PZ
Tel: 01823 653777   Fax: 01823 216796
email: sales@halsgrove.com
website: www.halsgrove.com

Printed in Great Britain by
The Cromwell Press Ltd, Wiltshire

Contents

Introduction

MERLIN is the true tale of a black leopard loosed into the British countryside by its owner, from a captive situation. This was a fairly common occurrence following The Dangerous Wild Animals Act 1976, which brought tighter legislation to bear on exotic pet owners.

However, escapes and releases of a variety of cat species have occurred for many years, no doubt from private collections for centuries, and to more recent times. Thus many tales of strange creatures have become part of our folklore and legend with numerous extraordinary sightings well documented.

During the 1980s the legend grew when media hype focussed on large numbers of sheep killed on Exmoor, allegedly by big-cats of the puma and leopard type including possible hybrids. Thus "The Beast of Exmoor" was born and if reports could be believed, as many as "80 sheep killed in 90 days", suggested animals of huge cunning and ferocity were loose on the moor. No one animal would kill and eat huge portions of meat in such a short period of time, and no small cats could do so. Cats 'as big as large calves, mastiffs and Alsatians' were seen all over the moor and beyond, the situation becoming rather silly in terms of reality, sizes becoming distorted and exaggerated by over enthusiasm and the average person's inability to gauge the size of a moving, distant animal. Often reported sightings were of "black" big-cats seen in darkness, or the glare of head-lights on country roads when shadows cast tend to add to an animals real size.

Gradually the Dartmoor and Bodmin Big-cats joined the Exmoor "Beast" and people from all over the British Isles reported sightings of the animals, along with some usually blurred, hurriedly taken photographs and video camera footage. There was also a lot of hoaxing.

My own interest began briefly in 1969 when the Western Morning News published an article about a puma loose in the Plymouth area, by the late Evelyn Scott Brown, a writer of occasional newspaper articles who resided in Cornwall.

But it was in 1983 when I was asked to track a big-cat, or cats, seemingly involved in the Exmoor sheep killings that I took a closer interest in the whole story.

Since then I have seen black leopards and pumas at a number of locations, some from my own investigating of wild and not so wild places, some thanks to farmers and other folk prepared to say what they had witnessed, including cats with cubs. Some cats have been shot dead and the facts kept quiet, so to speak. The cats exist and are living in the wilds of the Westcountry and elsewhere, including Ireland and France for example.

My own interest lies mainly with the black cats. I have seen them singly and with cubs and sub adults on occasions and invariably they do their best, naturally, to avoid humans. It is my opinion they rarely if ever kill sheep. They live mainly on small mammals up to rabbit size but will take roe and red deer, pheasants, gulls and other creatures. They, like us, have to eat.

So I have written "Merlin" based on numerous actual sightings, adding them into a melting pot of real and likely scenarios to emerge as "one cat" and his life in the wild as a "release".

The locations where given are correct.

Remember, these cats are not out and about seeking to harm humans. If you see one, enjoy the moment, leave it alone, don't set your dog onto it or attempt to corner it. And do not shoot them, a wounded big-cat will almost certainly be a dangerous animal indeed. Happy cat watching.

Trevor Beer
North Devon
2008

1

Freedom!

JACK Wakely mopped his tanned, weather beaten brow as the hot sun of a drought summer beat mercilessly upon the roof of his battered Land Rover. There had been no rain for many days and the reservoir he was gazing out across shimmered in the July heat, the larch trees around its distant edge seeming to wave and wriggle in the haze, almost mirage-like.

The reservoir, usually full of water from Exmoor's rains and the inlet stream at one end looked worryingly low, a jigsaw moonscape of cracked mud showing all around it. Even the very knowledge of obvious water shortage made a body all the more thirsty Jack thought. He drank from a bottle of orange juice, holding the container to his mouth until the last dregs had cooled his parched throat, his free arm around a black cat seated by his side.

"This is it I'm afraid, Merlin old friend, the parting of the ways. It has been a good two years but you must find a life of your own now."

He hugged the cat close to his side, gazing across the man-made lake to the dense forestry beyond. There was a lump in his throat, an ache pervading his chest and stomach as the cat's eyes gazed into his own, reading him, reading his very soul was how it felt.

Jack Wakely rose, undoing the strong leather collar around the cat's neck, to pull it tight around his own wrist in safe keeping.

"Out then boy", he said with a low voice, husky with the dread of the moment. "Come on Merlin."

The cat leapt to the ground and gazed about. Feeling no restraint from collar and leash he sniffed at his owner of two years then wandered slowly to the water's edge. Again he looked back at Jack, then turning he dipped his jet black head, lapping the sun-warmed water thirstily. He saw swallows hawking insects, they also dipping at times to scoop water from its surface as they zoomed low in rapid flight. He heard his owner clamber into the Land Rover and waited to be called but the vehicle lurched forward and away to drive up across the reservoir side.

Jack Wakely drove without looking back, the landscape misty with the heat haze and the tears in his eyes, cursing under his breath as he saw two people up ahead of him. They waved him down and rubbing his eyes he stopped the vehicle, winding down the window to see what it was they wanted.

"Hay fever", he said, to explain his tear-filled eyes. "I'm full of it this year."

The two people, a man and woman of around fortyish, smiled and nodded understandingly.

The woman gazed at him wide eyed as he hid the collar and leash beneath his waterproof jacket.

"Didn't you know you were being stalked by a huge black cat?" she exclaimed. "We saw it come around the loop of the reservoir behind you. Like one of those in jungle films or on flashy advertisements on TV."

"It was certainly a big cat and all black", her companion agreed. "But as to stalking you I think it may have been coincidence that you came along the same time. It certainly didn't appear threatening. Went into those trees." He pointed and Jack followed his gaze to where Merlin had obviously hidden.

"No I didn't know a cat was following me", Jack replied truthfully. "Perhaps it was a farm moggie and just looked big in the heat haze. Things can look out of proportion."

"Oh no." The young woman was adamant. "We have cats and this was no moggie as you call them. This was close on two feet at the shoulders, not one foot, and long with a beautiful, thick upturned walking stick of a tail."

She had described Merlin well, Jack thought. He told them best they all left the animal to its own devices in that case and not tell anyone or there'd be undue panic.

The couple, from a nearby village, agreed. They turned and walked back to the car-park, Jack deep in thought as to how Merlin would fare, as he drove slowly behind them to their vehicle.

The decision to set the cat free had not been easy but the other choices, a zoo, or having him destroyed were not options he felt acceptable. New laws regarding the keeping of "Dangerous Wild Animals" were in force and they required, quite rightly he thought, much safer accommodation and restrictions on the keeping of such animals. It wasn't so much the expense but more where he lived at the edge of a village. With more teenagers moving in with families, more dogs and cats prowling about. Even some of the youths wandered along evening time hedges thinking country life was about .22s and peering into other people's gardens and barns.

He loved Merlin and the cat returned his friendship and affection. He had taken him on from a former girl friend who had owned two for the slick ad's the couple by his side had referred to. They had been purchased via some "black market" in exotic cats but he'd asked no details. Then he'd moved to Devon with capital from his and his late parents homes to try his hand at wildlife painting, and sculpture.

He looked back. There was no sign of Merlin.

"I see your vehicle is caged and well equipped for carrying dogs. Do you have dogs?" The woman eyed him quizzically.

She is sharp, Jack thought, wondering about tell tale signs but knowing he kept a spotlessly clean vehicle. There was a photo of Merlin in the glove compartment. Must get that out and into an album. He realised there was a bit to do at home to erase the months with Merlin. He ached for the cat, but twas done now.

"I did have a dog, but not now. Must get another, there's always one needing a home I guess." He smiled at the couple, wanting to get away yet not wanting to go home where he and the leopard had shared so much.

"Well we are Jane and Peter."

She gave him their address saying, "call in if you are passing. Kettle's always on".

They drove off. Jack sat in his vehicle staring at the distant reservoir through the windscreen. Then with a sigh he revved the engine, turned the vehicle and headed homeward.

2

Of Hobbies & Roe Deer

MERLIN lay watching the rough track where he had last seen his owner's vehicle disappear into the heat haze. He saw the shadows of the trees lengthen, creeping purple across parched brown grass that should be lush and green. The wriggling heat haze gradually dissipated with the setting of the sun and the cooling of the earth as dew began to form., the water drops sparkling blood red and orange in the sunset as the day gave way slowly to the night.

Nothing moved along the dirt road. The splash of a fish jumping in the now fiery orange reservoir water caught Merlin's gaze and the great cat rose to watch a bird hawking dragonflies in the last light of day.

Larger than the swifts, swallows and martins who also hunted insects over the water, the bird had scythe shaped wings as did they but it was larger. The bird was a male hobby falcon whose mate was incubating eggs in the old nest of crows high in a pine tree at the forest edge. The hobbies had arrived in April from the same vast Continent of Merlin's ancestors though the birds only wintered there, following the sun away from Britain each September.

The hobby had taken food to his mate, then eaten a house martin caught on the wing when Merlin had first arrived. Now he chased and caught a golden ringed dragonfly, holding it tight as he swooped towards his Exmoor forestry home, filled with the joy of living, to perch in a pine tree adjoining the nest where sat his mate on their eggs.

The sun dipped further, sending a last sheet of flame colour along the horizon and the hobby saw a black shadow emerge from the trees to move slow and silent by the water's edge. His tired dark eyes closed to the night as the call of a tawny owl sounded from the trees nearby, it being the time

The bird was a male hobby falcon.

of nocturnal hunters of the fields and forests.

Merlin yawned and stretched, relishing in the coolness of a fine evening, his keen eyes seeing well, as well as the owl he could hear calling from the tree shadows. His every sense was alert as he reached up along a slightly leaning conifer, digging his sharp claws into the bark as he scratched and stretched his powerful muscles. Merlin was hungry and there was no man-friend to feed him his usual meal of fresh meat. Briefly he glanced in the direction of the dirt road for he could still smell his man-friend's scent, though it was fading swiftly with the dew.

A bat flew low over his head, then another, Daubenton's or Water bats who had spent the day in a hollow tree at the forest edge. Above the black leopard they flew to hawk insects over the reservoir lake as they did each early evening, Merlin unaware he had been struck by pulses of sound emitted through the mouths of the bats in their echo-location method of seeking objects to avoid, or to eat.

Merlin moved on, padding softly, head down, eyes and ears focussed ahead, sure of his strength and fitness, unsure of the new terrain, but the perfect hunting cat searching the night. The distant sound of a vehicle came to his ears but it was a sound he was used to and he paid it no heed, moving on to where a wide forestry ride lay as an earth road before him. Two deep vehicle tracks stretched ahead into the darkness and Merlin walked along one of these, sniffing the air.

In the long field adjoining the forest a small group of roe deer fed quietly. A full moon now lit the landscape but the roe fed at ease, used to the peace of the place, the dark forest close by them should they need to hide. Bracken at the forest edge was high, with young, tender grasses growing in its shade. Three deer fed here for there was no need to break cover with such succulent fare available. The grass beyond was dry and unpalatable due to the drought, the four roe deer feeding in the open, browsing on bramble leaves.

Roe are fastidious feeders, picking and choosing, never eating voraciously. Now with the drought the deer had taken more to drinking at the reservoir edge, or at the inlet stream, though they usually found sufficient water for their needs in lush vegetation.

It was thus that Merlin found them, feeding and unaware of his presence as he reached the forest edge, his black pelage part of the shadows, the slight breeze blowing deer scent to his twitching nostrils.

The moon became obscured by cloud, rain threatening from the south-west but desperately needed by every tree, shrub and blade of grass, every wild flower, every creature in the land.

Then came the sound of a distant shot, the sound echoing along the valley as a fusillade of noise. The roe deer moved as one, breaking into an immediate gallop towards the trees where Merlin now crouched, every muscle aquiver. The onslaught of sight and sound of stampeding animals almost overwhelmed his senses for it has to be remembered he had been captive reared and hand fed for most of his years.

And then the last of the fleeing deer was upon him and level, about to gallop by, and Merlin charged from the shadows and struck, the two animals rolling over and over until they hit a tree.

Merlin rose. The roe deer, a young buck, was dead, its back broken on impact with the tree, the leopard following ancient instincts of hunting from ambush. Merlin sniffed at the carcase and dragging it away from the tree roots, into the darkest shadows, he fed hungrily.

An hour later, his hunger assuaged, the cat moved stealthily down to the inlet creek and drank deeply, the remains of the roe deer already hidden from view beneath conifer brashings.

Then he moved away as the first pattering of rain for several weeks fell upon a parched landscape. He found an old shippon with a closed door but with some of the cob wall to the side fallen away. All was silent save for the welcome rain drops falling on his sleek, black coat. He went inside, finding straw and old hessian sacks in one corner and lying down was swiftly asleep.

3

Feuding Times
an Exmoor Incidental

THREE men stood in the shadows of a stand of trees at the head of an Exmoor coombe overlooking a farm track. They had two pairs of lurchers with them, a pair of deerhound cross greyhounds and a pair of pit bull crosses. The dogs sat silently by their owners, bred for power and speed, two working together able to bring down red deer.

Hidden just inside a field gateway was an old former Post Office mail van, its two sides hand painted in black gloss to cover the former Royal Mail insignia. The men were loggers by day, working woodlands under contract then selling the logs to people who still joyed in the luxury of log fires and bread toasted to perfection on long handled toasting forks. The growth of central heating in houses, and electric fires with simulated logs, reduced their profits drastically and the men had accordingly increased their forays into the countryside to poach and sell their wares to local inns and hotels for cash.

"It'll be dark soon. Blimmin good job too, I'm dyin' for a pint."

It was the younger of the three men who spoke. Short and wiry of build he had reached thirty years as a jobbing gardener and logger by trade, doing a bit of beating on a local estate renowned for its pheasant shoots, for perks.

"Us'll get our pints in soon enough Mick, don't ee fret. But this is the perfect night for this job and ee's got to pay for not letting us take 'is deer any more. Nice bit of rain cloud coverin' the moon tonight, just the job boy."

Harry was the eldest, a stocky man, wide shouldered and dark eyed. Like the others he was dressed in green and brown camouflage ex Army jacket, trousers and boots purchased from the Army and Navy Surplus Stores in the nearby town. He looked at his brother Tom, a tall, thin, silent man and Mick's father.

"Aye", Tom said. We'd better way get it done and out of the way now us ev agreed tis the way. Us knows us ev been treated rough. I don't know what's come over George lately, us ev always looked after'n.

"Well us'll look after'n tonight alright and a few more times then us'll pick up on some deer in the week easy enough." Harry smiled grimly, his gnarled hands clenched on his blackthorn walking stick.

"George asn't been the same since ees maid come back from University & Agricultural College. Good maid er is but soft on the bliddy deer, that's er trouble. An er don't miss nort gwane round on that horse of ers, she sees everything that's gwane on.

Mick snorted. "Huh! Us knows all that, we've talked it out enough times. Let's get the business done, I'm fed up standin' yer."

Out of the trees the men stepped, the dogs following close to heel. Very little light showed the way but the men had allowed their eyes to become accustomed to the swiftly gathering night, easily making their way to a gate at the bottom of the field which they opened to let the four dogs in. Somewhere close by a tawny owl hooted as the men loosed the dogs and stood back to watch.

It was past ten that night when they strolled casually into the local village pub, Mick greeting the landlord who poured them their three pints of "Best Bitter".

"Much doing chaps?" he enquired jovially.

"Busy enough Dave, busy enough." Mick grinned. "Us'll ev a pasty each if they'm hot."

He paid for the food and drink, nodding as the landlord ordered two loads of logs for the huge grate fire's autumn consumption.

In the field they had recently left, four full grown ewes lay dead by a hedge. The remainder of the flock huddled close together in an opposite corner, and George Jones and his wife Mary sat in armchairs, watching the News on the television. Next to them curled up on a settee their daughter Julie was reading a novel and looking forward to bed and days on the farm to come.

"Eye witnesses have reported seeing a large black cat-like animal crossing a road near Challacombe on Exmoor today. The animal is said to be the size of a Labrador dog and it was seen to leap up and over a hedge seven feet high. Police are asking anyone who sees such an animal to report it to them immediately. There have been no reports of any zoos or circuses losing their animals but the eye witnesses are adamant their sighting was of a huge cat, in broad daylight. Tomorrow's weather ......"

Julie stared at her parents.

"Where was that cat on the moor? I didn't catch what was said at the beginning Mum."

"Oh, a good ten miles from here dear. More up round Uncle Bill's way. Fancy a hot drink? It'll be a dog for certain, or somebody's black sheep. Huge black cat. Whatever next."

George Jones grinned. "You never know. Remember that crocodile two chaps saw on a marsh a few years ago? And there was they porcupines, that was in North Devon too, and wallaby. Cripes, what's it coming too."

4

Beast Hunt

GEORGE Jones was a worried man. He and his wife Mary farmed on the Exmoor fringes just inside the National Park. Farming tends to be a "worry" occupation these days in any case so any added worries caused tension twixt loved ones, relatives and friends and often the local community generally.

George was a worried man because he was losing sheep on a regular basis on his farm, not from disease but evidently from a predatory animal's occupation of his farmstead. The evidence such as it was included dead sheep ripped open at the head and shoulder areas and at the back end, the carcases bloodied and with considerable amounts of meat eaten from them. He recalled the recent radio broadcast.

It was 1983. A spate of sheep killings included such media tales as "80 sheep killed in 90 days", suggesting an animal or animals of undoubted power and ferocity inhabiting the wilds of Exmoor, one with an extraordinary appetite, or many mouths to feed.

Rogue dogs. That was the first likely predator of sheep. All farmers knew, from National Farmers Union reports, that several thousand sheep each year were killed by dogs. It was common knowledge and one of the aggravating aspects of farming.

But eye-witness sightings of strange cat-like animals of large size were being reported, some in the vicinity of George Jones' farm. Black, dark brown and grey to fawn animals the size of pumas were being seen, and the stories were getting around. So a few people jawing away, the way people do reckoned that big-cats were to blame for the sheep kills and that was newspaper sales and ratings increases for the local media.

So was born the "Beast of Exmoor", with artist's impressions of huge toothed and clawed black, monstrous cat-like creatures as well as photographs of pumas, leopards and such gracing newspaper pages and TV screens throughout the land.

The police became involved, with one particular sergeant collating evidence from Exmoor and surrounding farmland. Sightings of big-cats increased, many people reporting day time and night time glimpses, some of huge cats as big as calves, most of which probably were calves.

George Jones organised a "shoot" at his farm one early spring day, informing the police and asking one or two local naturalists to help track the "Beast" or perhaps identify tracks.

Several "guns" were present, and sightseers, and a Police helicopter. At one stage of the day much shouting and some shooting occurred. Almost a frenzy of noise. An animal had run up a tree in view of the "guns" and had been pursued and shot. It was a mink, full grown it was true but of no size, nor was it capable of killing sheep, not even lambs.

There were no tracks to be identified. Such was the mass invasion of people across the farm and its environs that muddy gateways that may have yielded tracks were trampled by people and dogs.

Their "Beast Hunt" begun at 10 am was over and done by lunch time. Any self respecting big-cat would have been long gone by 10.05 am, more likely well before the hunt began.

On the day of the "Beast Hunt" on Exmoor, Merlin was resting up on National Trust land 30 miles away. He was not on Exmoor and had eaten of a deer killed the evening before as it limped painfully by a lake surrounded by woods. The red deer was slowly dying of gangrene in its haunch, caused by a cross-bow bolt fired by a poacher. The deer had died swiftly as Merlin leapt from ambush, watched by squawking herons nesting in the trees above, bringing the yearling hind down with his running charge. He had dragged the carcase into bushes, eaten his fill and left her covered by vegetation he had pulled about her body following his meal. In all the time following his release Merlin the black leopard had never killed a sheep.

5

A Fishy Tale

BRIAN and Stan were fishing pals with a special love for night fishing. Their wives were happy "angling widows" with a special love for TV Soaps and the occasional G & T. Contentment reigned, the men sitting beside reservoirs and fishing lakes, their spouses beside log fires and television, alternating venues each weekend.

"This is the life Stan. Brown trout in our favourite little hot spot. I like this dam corner, insects pushed by the prevailing wind, a bit of warm surface water. Makes for good fishing. And tis lovely here after sunset even if we don't catch much."

"Yeah, yeah, yeah. I love it too. This dry fly fishing when trout are rising suits me. I've got eight nice ones. All caught on that Black Muddler." Stan was satisfied and a beer under the stars, washing down a home made pasty of immense proportions was the perfect end to a perfect day.

"Yes. Eight is good. I've got five beauties too. It was a good idea to keep fishing this reservoir until we soused out the right places Stan. I think we've got the knack of retrieves now. I found those little four or five inch jerks just right today. That big one that followed the fly in waited til I'd swept the rod to one side and the fly went parallel with the bank. I must remember that ploy."

The two men chatted on about droppers and bob flies and the delight of pasties and a real ale.

"Look there's Orion and Sirius up there. What a sky. Let's stay another hour or so and go home, shower and watch a late night film Brian. I've got a bottle of Grouse in."

"Sounds good to me Stan. 'The Big Sleep' is showing on Sky tonight."

"Yeah. And here too. I'm feeling yawny already."

"Good job we cleaned the trout. A final clean when we get home, and into the freezer."

"Yeah, you stock this lot. I'll stock the next."

The two friends became silent. Somewhere a tawny owl hooted and its mate replied. A gentle breeze riffled the water surface and away in the distance a fox screamed. Brian sipped his drink. Sunday tomorrow, he thought. Breakfast and a newspaper. Lunch, out for a drive with Jean. Where was it she wanted to go? The garden centre, that was it. Hanging basket time. Stan was the vegetable gardener. Fresh fish and fresh vegetables, really good stuff too, and always shared. Ansome stuff.

He settled back in his comfortable fishing chair and stretched his legs, taking another drink of ale.

A pebble rattled by his side and he could hear heavy breathing. Stan was dozing off. He's almost purring, Brian thought. Must be thinking of the Grouse whisky. Maybe a hot toddy.

"What?" Stan's voice startled him. "What do you want Brian? Just say. Don't nudge me. I almost jumped out of me skin."

"Whaddayamean? I have'nt moved. I thought you were dozing off."

"I thought you were. Oi, stop nudging my shoulder. How do you do that from there?" Stan sounded genuinely puzzled.

Brian turned his head towards his friend and a chill went through him. Stan was sitting back in his chair and behind him just to one side was a huge black animal its round powerful head on a level with Stan's.

Brian's legs turned to iced water. He stared hard. The animal was real, not a figment of his imagination or the result of strong ale. It was a big black cat. A very big black cat. He saw the animal lean forward to strike Stan's shoulder again. It was sniffing him.

"Stan." His voice croaked hoarsely. "Don't move an inch. Trust me."

"There you go again Brian. Quit nudging me."

"Stan. You know when I'm being very serious. Just keep very still I'm telling you."

"You're whispering you mean. Why whisper? What can you see? Is there an otter in the water. I can't see it. Tell me what it is. Where is it?" Stan leaned forward very slowly to stare out across the lake.

Brian was considering a massive leap into the water.

"Don't sit back again Stan. Keep very still and keep staring at the water."

Brian tensed both arms, gripping the chair as hard as he dared, tensing his leg muscles to jump.

"Stan. I'm about to jump straight out and into the lake mate. When I do, you do exactly the same. That black Beast of Exmoor thing is right behind you. It's huge. Now, on the count of three, together, into the lake. One, two, three!"

Brian leapt up and out of his chair, straight into the lake, landing at least five feet from the bank up to his chest in freezing water. "Do it!" he screamed, turning to face the bank.

"You actually did it! You're bonkers! How much bloody ale have you had? You didn't expect me to fall for that, did you? And why did you jump in anyway. Why not just see if I was daft enough to believe you?"

Brian stared at Stan. The big-cat was gone. His leap and shout must have frightened it away. He waded spluttering, freezing, soaking and still very scared up out of the water.

"I was not joking Stan. I'm not so daft as to leap in myself am I? I tell you the Beast of Exmoor was nudging you on the shoulder, not me. I was sitting too far away. Urgh! I'm soaked bloody through man. Let's get home quick."

"You jumped up thinking I'd jump in the lake, and you slipped and fell in." Stan roared with laughter. "Well it was spectacular I must say. Didn't think to see a flounder in a reservoir. Oi my two spare pasties have gone."

"So have mine. What did I tell you?"

Stan stared at his soaking friend. They quickly gathered up their gear and trout and ran for their car, tumbling in and slamming shut the doors.

Brian was shivering. "Home and not a word to the ladies. I'll sneak upstairs quick and have a hot shower and change. This'll take the whole bottle of Grouse between us mate."

"Good job I've bought two then. I 'm beginning to believe you but you could have hidden the pasties."

Merlin watched the vehicle light disappear into the distance. All was silent again save for the owls calling. For a brief moment he recalled a human friend with just such a noisy vehicle. But he'd eaten four pasties and head low he followed the track to the old shippon and was soon asleep on his bundle of sacks.

Later as he slept, two men and two women sat sipping whisky by a log fire, waiting for the late film. On the local news was a report of sightings of a large black cat earlier that week, and the picture of a reservoir.

Brian nodded to Stan and raised his glass. "Cheers mate", they said in unison.

Inevitably, soon after the news of a black big-cat at Wistlandpound reservoir was broadcast so people popped up from behind every tree, bush and stone wall.

Various guns were seen, even a man with a .22 air pistol, and many camera enthusiasts. As ever there were hoaxers including two newspaper camera-men who should have known better.

Trackers were seen. A man dressed up as a shrub kept vigil until a large black retriever cocked its leg and soaked him, a double shock for he had at first thought the dog appearing out of the early morning mist was the big cat, so he retired ungracefully from the scene.

Merlin left Wistlandpound on the morning after the incident with the anglers so he did not see or hear the hue and cry his presence had aroused.

Brian and Stan said not a word about Brian's leap into the lake but they took up river fishing, and in daylight only from that day on. As Stan said when the one that got away was a black leopard it's a story to quietly chat about twixt themselves.

A black big-cat was seen crossing the road at Blackmoor

Gate by a couple driving home one late night and "another" was seen along a green lane in the parish of East Down by a naturalist and his young female colleague. As luck would have it the Blackmoor Gate sighting was passed on to the naturalist, who said nought about it nor about the green lane sighting, so no further hue and cry ensued.

Thus it was that Merlin had come to Arlington Court Estate ...

6

Arlington

MISTY rain swept almost horizontally across a man made lake where two grey herons stood shoulders hunched, backs to the weather as is the way of herons. The gaunt, grey birds had hatched that early spring from bluish eggs laid in a huge stick nest in the trees by the lake.

There were thirty heron's nests in the tree tops, the heronry an ancient site of these colonial nesters, so much so that effigies of the species perched on gateposts at the entrance to the large estate. It had once been owned by a great family of the area until the last of the line, a delightful woman who loved wildlife, left it to the National Trust as a gift to the nation, as a nature reserve , for people to visit and enjoy.

Merlin lay in the shelter of a hide overlooking the lake where a few grey lag geese and twenty mallard drifted slowly in the rain-swept breeze ripples forever spreading out from a water inlet. He had eaten one each day for three days, caught whilst they slept, head beneath one wing on the lake bank beside a stone obelisk. Mallard soon forget.

With the coming of the rain the few people visiting the estate had tended to congregate in and around the great house with its many treasures, and a carriage collection, shop and restaurant. To walk the wet though beautiful mile down to the lake could wait for sunny day visits and thus was the hide undisturbed at such times.

In the wildest imaginings of previous owners there would have been no thought given to a black leopard living wild on a Devonshire estate. Nor would such a possibility have been entertained by the National Trust staff capably going about their various indoor and outdoor tasks on a rainy summer's day but there Merlin was and there he had been for over a week.

He had become excited at times by the scent of horses passing by but the rumble of carriage wheels and shouting of humans deterred him from possible horse flesh meals. On his second day at the site he had killed and eaten from a tiny shetland pony in a marshy field by the roadside. On the third day he had eaten again from the kill but on the fourth day the carcase had been stripped clean by rats and a scavenging buzzard. It now lay like the remains of a timber built boat in the lush grass and balsam flowers adjoining the Yeo river, unseen by the National Trust staff who occasionally counted the ponies and Jacob's sheep that "pleased" visitors, or went about the business of forestry above the lake.

Merlin had eaten well at Arlington thus far, more than was necessary to keep him content and his days were easy and mainly restful. Sheep there were in plenty but he did not like sheep, disliking the mouthfulls of wool from his one and only attempt at mutton meals, though that kill, too, had been exploited by fox, buzzard, raven and brown rat scavengers within hours.

Such a carcase, with big-cat spoor around and about, and a few hairs examined by so-called experts, immediately gave the cat an undeserved reputation as "the" sheep killer of the region. People love to put two and two together to make five, or even six but the truth of it all was that Merlin was not a killer of sheep, nor of other livestock. Rabbits, pheasants, and smaller prey were easy to come by along with wildfowl, truly wild or otherwise.

Merlin rose and stretched. He felt good. He was in prime condition and free. Sunlight shone through the hide windows and the rain had ceased. He was to leave Arlington, never to return to the area as part of his current, huge territory.

7

Deer Poachers

MERLIN killed a red deer calf on his way from Arlington towards the adjoining rural parish of East Down. It was a moment of swift dawn light ambush as deer moved on pattering hooves out of dense woodland, frightened by the back- firing of a green painted vehicle used by forestry staff. The deer moved away from the seeming "gun-shot", to trot beneath trees where Merlin lay slumbering along the vast branch of an ancient oak tree.

Suddenly scenting the big-cat the leading hind rolled her eyes, snorted and broke into a gallop followed immediately by the rest of the group. Sixteen strong in all, eleven hinds and five calves they had galloped swiftly below Merlin's resting place and he had virtually fallen upon the last in line, smothering its groans with powerful jaws over its mouth and nostrils, his tearing claws ripping the life from the young Exmoor born deer.

Hearing the vehicle close by Merlin clasped the yearling in his powerful jaws and leapt scrambling back up into the massive oak. He ate hungrily of the still warm deer, tearing massive mouthfuls of fresh meat from the succulent carcase until his hunger was stilled.

More shots, this time from actual guns. Merlin rose uneasy. It was time to leave this place of plenty and he dropped lithely to the ground to move at a rapid lope along the woodland path, leaving the deer carcase ten feet high, caught in the fork twixt branch and tree trunk.

Another shot sounded and Merlin increased his pace as soil and stones leapt up, striking his face and neck. When he was close beneath a tall hedgerow he sprang high, clearing the hawthorns growing atop the earth bank in one mighty bound, to run on through a crop field on the other side, to reach a dark, silent forestry plantation and safety.

"Hells bells! That was one of them big-cats we've been reading about Charlie. I nearly had it too."

"Yeah. And we'd better get out of here fast. Our shots will have been heard I reckon and we've got nothing to show for it neither," Charlie replied. "Let's make tracks afore us gets ourselves caught."

The two deer poachers worked as a team, sometimes with two colleagues, supplying venison, salmon and ought else they could sell at the back doors of a few hotels in Somerset. To poach Devon side, as they called it, was useful from time to time as they and their vehicle were too well known in the Somerset and Avon area.

Charlie was the older member of the group, skilled with a powerful catapult, firing ball bearings when it was needed, a virtually silent killer that had taken many a night roosting pheasant from trees at wood edges.

Now he drove swiftly along well known country roads until they came out onto a dual carriageway that stretched northward for miles. He breathed a sigh of relief and settled back in his seat chewing on an unlit pipe.

"Are we going to look around that Nature Reserve area Charlie? There's deer there usually and it's not well wardened." Ben, his companion eyed the older man eagerly.

"Not bliddy likely we're not. You're getting careless Benny. A few good weeks and you get over confident. You'll ev us caught, you will, anyway the owner's a naturalist chap and often there night times, he's pretty sharp and no mistake".

Ben glowered. It was his second year of heavy poaching. Before that he'd lamped with lurchers around his home village until he'd strayed further afield and got caught by Charlie and his two pals. They had roughed him up for poaching "their" patch and sent him home bruised in body and ego. Then one night as he sat with a pint of ale in his local, his two lurchers at his feet, Charlie had walked in alone and recognising him, had got chatting.

The two men had much in common so had gotten along. Charlie, who had "lost" his favourite companion took Ben under his wing and the partnership had gelled in the main, apart from Ben's occasional bursts of headstrong-ness. Blood rushes, Charlie called them, but he genuinely feared Benny would get them caught one of these days.

Charlie chewed on his pipe as he drove. He was considering retiring from the group and going his own way as he used to. You never get caught on your own out in the dark. He'd had keepers walk by in the woods, and water bailiffs. Once he'd pushed a man hard down a slope and into the river, a chap he didn't like from the nearby town. Mostly he didn't care either way, the chaps were doing their job and his job was not to get caught.

Ben was humming a tune. He soon forgot his grumbles. He was actually good with dogs and good to them.

Funny thing about the black big-cat, Ben thought. What's it coming to with them things about in the dark. And up trees too. They'd have a dog before it knew what hit'n. Creepy. He thought of the times he'd hidden under or in trees. Now you might have a bliddy leopard or puma sat beside you. Course, they'm just as likely to ketch a keeper or bailiff. He chuckled aloud.

"What is it Benny?" Charlie asked.

"Nort really. I'm just thinking about that cat us saw. Twas quite a big un. Wouldn't want to run up against one in the dark."

"Nor in daylight, come to that Charlie, I've just been thinking too. What if twas wounded a bit? Twould be a right devil of an animal then."

"Yep. Just you remember that. No wild shooting or any more careless actions. Tid'n worth it."

"No I know you'm right Charlie. This chasing around is getting on my nerves too. June's getting worried about it and is pushing me to keep to window cleaning and gardening for folks."

June was Benny's girl friend. A lovely, warm hearted country girl full of fun and a laugh a minute. She was barmaid at Benny's local and a good catch as a partner and wife.

Charlie said, "sensible sort is June, you're a lucky chap there. I'm thinking of packing it in anyway. Getting too old and tid'n like it used to be. That cat's got me thinking. Black as night and they say there's a few of em about Benny."

"Aye. Bit worrying. Don't want to wake up daid do us Charlie. I never expected to run up against jungle animals round yer. Anyways if you'm giving up I may's well do the same. I've learned a lot from ee Charlie and us can still have a weekend pint together."

"That I like Benny. D'you know I actually feel ten yers younger. There'll always be pheasant or salmon, or game pie on the table if you and June comes to dinner. And twill be fresh."

Benny laughed aloud. "I knows that Charlie. And at my place too. Funny isn't it, that bliddy cat, turning up. Got us both all cautious like. I'm glad. June will be glad."

The two men settled back in the vehicle seats, the road into north Somerset speeding beneath them.

By noon of the day the two men were at home in their respective cottages mulling over the recent events.

By noon of the same day Merlin was sound asleep in a broken down timber built shed, on old hessian sacks and leaves, dry and warm, already eight miles away from Arlington, with rows of conifers all about. Above him the twittering of swallows in their nest was unheard in the soundness of the cat's sleeping.

A week later a forestry worker on the Arlington Estate found the deer carcase lodged in a tree fork, part eaten by two carrion crows nesting nearby, and now fly ridden. The forester phoned a local naturalist and so was Merlin's whereabouts recorded on a map of the area along with numerous other big cat sightings in the region.

On that same day Merlin reached the North Devon coast.

8

Coastal Haunts

THE shooting incident had driven Merlin towards the coast, the cat moving by night to reach a hilltop via a farm known as 6 Acres where he had sprayed a standing stone erected thousands of years before. The cat did not know that the "pull" which brought him to this spot was due to his following a ley, a powerful line of earth magnetism, one of many criss crossing the land.

Once people had followed leys as easily as animals still do today but now only a few in every thousand held close to nature, feeling and to a point understanding the magic of the earth and its powers.

Thus Merlin came to the Valley of Rocks on a night of the full moon. He had eaten two young rabbits in the hour before midnight as they dozed in the coolness of a path through brambles by Woolhanger pond. Then, drinking from the pond he had moved on, startling four horses stabled close by a house, so much so they had lashed out with hooves, kicking stable boxes until their owners had lit the area with outdoor lights and sent two boxer dogs to see who or what was about disturbing the peace.

The two powerful boxers had rushed out at their owners' bidding then turned back to almost bowl them over as they returned to the house door, wide eyed and trembling.

"Something's spooked the horses, and now the dogs Jenny." The man who spoke from the stable looked about the grounds, lit as bright as day by the moon and his security lighting but there was nothing to be seen.

"Stray dog about, perhaps", his wife replied, but she saw the boxers were wanting to go back indoors. Not at all like them, she thought.

A barn owl screeched loud, the ghostly white bird flying silently over the lawns on downy feathers, then it screeched again, an answering call coming from their home in a nearby barn loft.

"Those two probably. They make me jump sometimes."

The man placated the horses, checked all was locked up and wandered back to the house, whistling happily.

"Perhaps a combination of things dear", he said to his wife. "What with the owls, and the badgers often about, and that full moon. Enough to put the creeps up the best of us. Funny things full moons. Let's go find a nightcap."

"Sounds good to me. You pour and I'll settle Rex and Jake."

Deep in the Valley of Rocks, close to a rock formation known as the Devil's Cheesewring, Merlin padded along the hillside to find himself in Mother Meldrum's Kitchen, a snug cave in the rocks where he curled up and promptly fell asleep, totally unaware of the folklore significance of the area, or that an old woman had once lived where he lay, during summer months.

9

Of Wild Goats & Things

THE silver grey ghost of dawn light and the sound of human voices awoke Merlin to a new day. He gazed about him at old stone walls and part of a large buck rabbit carcase from his meal the night before. Rising, he nosed at it then with a sweep of one forepaw sent it rolling against the open door of Duty Point tower close to the Valley of Rocks.

Merlin had moved from Mother Meldrum's kitchen when a young boy, one of a group of holidaymakers threw a large stone into his hideout. Outside, two adults and another child were laying out chicken legs and sandwiches for a picnic after a day's sightseeing in the town of Lynton nearby.

"What are you up to Kyle? Stop throwing stones."

"There's a funny black dog in here. Now it's looking at me dad. Why's a dog in this cave place?"

The boy clattered another stone into the ancient dwelling of the old wise woman who had once lived here in summer months of the year. She had become part of the Lorna Doone tale of outlaws and romance, a soothsayer visited by Jan Ridd, hero of R.D. Blackmoor's book, now a tourism hook for the area.

"I said stop that stone throwing Kyle. Let me come and look at this dog you are on about." The man grunted and rose from his seat against the rock, warmed by the sun.

As the man's large shadow fell into the rock cavern Merlin rose and stretched. The second stone had bounced and hit his left ear and the cat was irritated. He saw a man's head and shoulders appear and gave a coughing grunt of a snarl, crouching ready to spring.

"Bloody hell! Get out of here quick. Pick Emily up and just go. Kyle, get off down to the car with the others. Now!!!

The man's last command was loudly shouted. Merlin stepped towards him, seeing him turn to grab the smaller human, and he moved into the sunlight to watch four hurrying figures scrambling down the steep stony hillside to where a road and many shimmering vehicles showed a car park and people.

Merlin growled. Moving forward he caught the scent of food. He ate eight sandwiches and four chicken legs then sniffed at custard tarts and apples which he left. He nosed into the wicker picnic basket and ate more sandwiches, then lifting his head gazed down the hillside.

"There it is! That isn't a dog, it's a big zoo cat that's got loose or something."

The man with his wife and two children pulled them along the road to where a track cut across a road traffic roundabout. Other people were staring and pointing. Merlin ambled down the track towards the road as the man selling ice creams and cold drinks slammed down the open window at the counter of his van and leapt for the driving seat. The long queue, seeing the large black cat, disappeared rapidly towards their respective vehicles with much pointing and slamming of doors.

Suddenly all was quiet, without people noise. Two buzzards soared high over the rocky valley from a woodland nest of sticks opposite Lee Abbey, enjoying the warm sunshine on spread wings.

Merlin could hear swifts, house martins and swallows swarming, hawking insects high above him and then he whirled, snarling, hearing the thunder of hooves on hard rock. He whirled again, every instinct alert as a large, dark, galloping shape passed him, the animal itself whirling about to bear down again on the leopard who had now leapt high onto a huge flat rock the better to assess this sudden attack. He snarled, striking angrily at the rolling-eyed dark face with a pair of huge horns atop its head, his sharp claws barely missing the snorting beast's nostrils.

The horned beast was King of a tribe of wild goats that had lived in the Valley of Rocks for many years, possibly

The horned beast was king of the tribe of wild goats.

long before, when the town of Lynton had but a few houses and few people. His ancestors, together with the sheep and ox was one of the earliest domesticated animals to reach these shores, probably during the Neolithic era when the British Isles were still joined to the continental land mass.

To Merlin, the King of the goat tribe stank. His nostrils flared at the urine scents wafting from the great goat's beard. His eyes raged but the goat was not going to give ground. Merlin felt no fear but he could hear the clattering of falling rocks and of hooves on stone as others of the tribe gathered about to see this strange black animal in their domain. Their leader squirted more urine forward, some splattering on his beard, some onto the sun warmed rocks.

Merlin uttered a scream of rage which carried loudly to the ears of the human watchers below. He knew he could do great damage to the goat but he wanted no injuries, for that would likely mean he could not hunt to feed. He swung a clawed forepaw once again at the staring face of the goat and as it whirled away to avoid the blow Merlin was already down from his rock vantage point and bounding along parallel with the road that here was once a river cut by the Ice Age.

Minutes later found him on a coastal cliff path where grew gorse and sea campion. He found himself at an old stone built tower with windows looking out to sea. A stonechat called, "chack chack", from the top of a gorse bush, telling his mate to keep silent upon their five eggs in a nest built low into the bush stem.

Merlin could hear kittiwake calls. He saw fulmar petrels gliding on stiffly held wings and he nosed through the open door of the tower, finding himself in relatively peaceful snugness with no smell of goat. He laid down facing the open doorway and was soon asleep.

Thus it was that he had come to "The Lonely Tower" visited in the nineteenth century by the great English landscape artist, Samuel Palmer, and used by him for some of his paintings. Merlin did not know of such things though

Samuel Palmer would have known of other Merlins, of King Arthur and of Tintagel in Cornwall which he was later to visit and paint "in approaching rain".

10

Of Otters, Adders & Walkers

TYPICALLY the long weeks of drought in England were followed by heavy August rains. But they brought an unusual peace to the countryside as people who would normally have thronged to farmland and beaches wandered morosely about wet, gleaming townships, gladdening the hearts of shop and restaurant owners who often prayed to their respective gods for wet weather and full premises.

Merlin had moved from the farming estate of Lee Abbey for it was a busy site with humans and dogs always about. He had followed the hogs-back cliff path westwards, living on rabbits for a week, caught near a waterfall that fell to the path from a cliff top above, and then on down to a tiny cove where seals sometimes rested from fishing in the sea.

It was here he had crouched amongst bracken fern to watch an otter swim from the waves and clamber up to within a few yards of where he lay, hidden by ferns. The animal, totally new to the watching leopard, lolloped along the path to the cascade of fresh falling water, to stand beneath its showering fall. Merlin crouched, relaxed. Something told him the otter was not food. He watched as the animal held its broad, flat head up into the fresh, cold, falling water, mouth opening and closing and then standing tall upon its brown furred haunches it carefully cleaned all vestiges of salt from its dense pelage.

The otter had eaten a large carp taken from the lake in the Hunter's Inn gardens, then a trout from the Heddon river nearby. Her two cubs of the year had moved on, dispersing early to find territories of their own. She was free now from hunting for and with them and had allowed the fresh water of the Heddon to carry her into the sea where she had drifted to reach the shingly cove and its cascade.

Now she washed the last salt of the sea from her coat and shaking herself vigorously she ran into the ferny vegetation on hearing human voices and was gone from Merlin's gaze amongst the heather, gorse and rock clitter.

Feeling the vibrations from human footfalls an adder slithered away from its sunbathing spot on the path to hide beneath bracken and await the passing of people. It was a black adder, as black as Merlin himself, a melanistic snake, one of many along this part of the coast.

A group of humans walked in single file led by local naturalists who took walking tour parties about the countryside as part of their living. The leader had seen the black adder glide away but said nothing for his group of thirty walkers were chatting happily away. He waited to give time for a rest and allow several with cameras to take pictures.

The group had walked from Woody Bay and would reach the Hunter's Inn for refreshments, or visit the National Trust shop for gifts for friends, and ice creams and Kendal Mint Cake. He grinned as his young companion who was back-marking the group came over to him, telling her about the adder. She nodded, staring up at the sparkling water falling many metres to the path where they stood.

It was a beautiful sight, the sun on water droplets, the ferns bobbing and dipping in the spray as high in the sky a buzzard circled on warm air currents. She raised her binocular, focussing, seeking a wren that had flitted about above the group, her favourite bird since childhood. Then she stiffened and gasped, only her companion noticing and he too raised his binocular to see what she'd found to cause her obvious surprise.

"There by the rock ledge", she whispered.

He too could see it clearly. Merlin's black, handsome face gazed down at them, his eyes golden-green in the bright sunlight, two white fangs just showing.

"Well, well, well. Time we made a move don't you think?"

"Definitely." The young woman smiled, the cat's presence their secret, the animal safe with the two of them.

Merlin's black, handsome face gazed down at them.

"Right then folks. Let's push on. I'll keep an eye open for peregrines on this next bit of coast. You never know what you might see hereabouts."

He moved away, the party resuming their single file chatty convoy, duly head-counted, the young woman bringing up the rear. "What a day", she smiled to herself.

Merlin watched them go, then dropping his head onto his forepaws he dozed, feeling the wren perch on his shoulders then flit away again into the surrounding herbage. Below them the black adder slid out to bask in its sun spot, the pathway silent and peaceful once more.

11

Dartmoor

MERLIN had reached Dartmoor following a route that brought him to the river Taw at Belstone, the same river that empties into the sea not many miles from where he had been set free at Wistlandpound Reservoir. The leopard was weary from travelling and avoiding people en route and now he lay in the warm sunshine on a huge granite outcrop.

He had slept the previous night hidden by a set of old stocks by Belstone village after tearing open a bin liner and eating chicken and several sandwiches, then a shoulder of cooked lamb only partly used at the Tors Inn. He had caught the scent of cooked food on the breeze and swiftly discovered the refuse bags now lying torn open near the Inn wall.

Merlin had awoke at daybreak to the sound of the dawn chorus of many birds and the barking of a sheepdog. A farm vehicle and trailer rumbled by and he had risen to lope away along a track passing a Treatment Works, on to the moor gate at Watchet to follow a track by a stone wall. A male kestrel perched upon the wall, a lizard hanging from its hooked beak, which he swallowed as he watched the cat go by. The kestrel's mate was sitting on a clutch of four densely speckled red-brown eggs in a crow's old nest in a nearby rowan tree.

As Merlin passed, a fat woodmouse scampered from beneath his paws and the kestrel pounced upon it, flying with his prey to the nest where he fed it to the female. The male falcon would feed his mate for about a month while she incubated their eggs, occasionally relieving her until the hatching of the eggs. For a further month both adults feed the young until they fly free to hunt with them for a while, before becoming independent of them.

Many small rodents, insects, frogs and lizards would die to feed kestrels but this part of Dartmoor was rich in wildlife, even to keeping a big-cat well fed and contented.

Merlin had passed by, following a grassy track to the northernmost outcrop on Watchet Hill, known as Tors End, and up he went to the next outcrop, following a ridge crest around the side of Belstone Tor, to come to the Irishman's Wall and thence to Higher Tor where rowan, whortleberry and moorland grasses seem to spring from the very granite.

A buzzard soaring high above, saw the big cat moving across the tor slope and closing his wings, swooped down for a closer look. Beating its powerful wings the raptor perched on a jutting rock then deciding the leopard was a prize too large to contemplate, launched from the perch to soar in circles on rising warm air currents.

Merlin padded on, passing a grass covered cairn and along a ridge to Knattaborough outcrop and the boundary of the Okehampton Firing Range. The sound of distant shooting caused him to hurry onward, head down, to reach Oke Tor, and on to cross the Taw river by a ford, then upstream to the ruins of Knack Mine. Here he sniffed at the carcase of a dead sheep, its bones picked clean by buzzards, and he whirled away at the sight of two humans, going back over the ford, to trot on to a lookout hut and a path to Wild Tor.

Merlin splashed through boggy ground, over Steeperton Brook, down to the ruins of an old tinner's house, then past Hound Tor. He found the track difficult to follow, eventually reaching a triple stone row and a wide open expanse of moorland, here unmarked by army vehicle tracks. The sound of army firing had ceased and Merlin killed a rabbit sunning itself by one of the many standing stones. He ate it where he stood, then moved across the moor to the summit of Cosdon Hill, once thought erroneously to be the highest point on the great moor. Here upon a sun warmed rock it was that he laid down to rest and doze the day away in peace.

12

Rambler Disturbance

MERLIN lay in the sunshine which had bathed Dartmoor for over two weeks. He had fed well on rabbits, and once on a hen pheasant caught by the double Kistvaen at the end of the Cosdon triple stone row. The leopard was in prime condition, the weather suiting him here on the wild moor in summertime.

But now with the increasing appearance of humans on the moor Merlin was becoming irritated and restless. He knew nought of such human matters as weekends, holidays and tourism, all he knew was that the peace he had found in this open, rugged terrain was being invaded by more and more people and it was time to move.

In fact several walkers had caught glimpses of the big-cat and once a roaring, rattling helicopter had swooped low over the stone row, forcing him to hide beneath rowans and bracken until the machine went away. Fortunately for Merlin local police had other things to do and when informed by members of the public, that big-cats were about the moor, they said, "the matter is in hand", and went on with their numerous everyday tasks.

Merlin had watched Dartmoor ponies feeding at times but on the one occasion he had rushed a foal as possible supper he had received a barrage of hooves and gnashing teeth from the stallion grazing by his mate and foal. Blows to one shoulder had thrown Merlin onto his side, glancing blows only, but they had taught him that there was easier prey on the moor than hardy Dartmoor ponies. Only his pride was hurt but as is the way of wild animals he learned to avoid danger and possible harm for an injured animal may swiftly become weak and die of injury and starvation.

At midday a party of twenty or more ramblers appeared at the far end of the stone rows to begin chatting and photographing the site. Merlin rose and slipped away, a black shadow of a big-cat unseen and silent. He loped southwards to Cut Hill, crossing two waterways where damselflies sparkled and glowed along the banks, then army vehicles and shouting men forced him eastward and he found himself in Fernworthy Forest beneath shade, and was soon drinking from the reservoir fed by the South Teign river. More people appeared along its banks and Merlin turned back into the green shade of the forest, the first to be planted on Dartmoor in 1919 by the Duchy of Cornwall. As he ran his great paws scattered many flint scraps telling of ancient man's itinerant industry on the moor. Soon he was amongst cooling trees, his feet on silent leaf fall, the sound of human voices gone. He found a fallen tree leaning against another and lithely ran up the broad trunk, finding a perfect platform of branches on which to lay and here he stretched out to doze and watch the forest all about and below, totally invisible from the ground.

"Sree srreee." The screechy, high pitched call came close by his ears and Merlin saw a tiny bird perched on a branch above his head. The goldcrest called again then began feeding on insects and small spiders caught in the fir bark crevices of the tree.

From another branch higher in the tree hung a hammock- like nest constructed like a small ball with an entrance hole near the top. Made of mosses, lichens and gossamer and lined with thistle down and feathers it had within it a female goldcrest incubating seven eggs. She would incubate the eggs for 18 days while the male keeps watch and sings its "dee-dullee, dee-dullee dee" song. Once the nestlings are hatched both parents will feed the young until they fly free at a further 18 days, a long time for such a tiny species.

It being June this was the second brood of the year, a family of eight goldcrests already fledged and about the conifer canopy.

Merlin listened to the goldcrest calls change to the song as the little male, finding the big cat no threat to his mate, continued to tell the world of their breeding territory in the way of birds. Merlin liked the sound and watching the goldcrests his eyes gradually closed and he slept.

13

Fernworthy

MIDSUMMER'S Eve. Merlin awoke with a start at the sound of human voices, low and murmuring some distance away and below him. It was only just daylight but dark in the forest shade, a green gloom that Merlin's eyes saw as grey, with the black vertical shapes of tree trunks all about. But other shapes moved in the shadows, and flickering lights showed, a phenomenon unknown to the big-cat, causing him to glare and to snarl silently, fangs bared as he contemplated yet another disturbed lair that hitherto had been so peaceful.

He watched from his tree branch platform that had been his main lair for many days, annoyed that his peace and happiness was disturbed at all but moreso that it was his time to hunt for a meal and there had been roe deer in the forest nearby that very day.

Within their hammock nest the goldcrests were fast asleep, nocturnal activities left to birds and other creatures of the night.

Merlin shifted and rose on his platform, the better to see what was occurring below. His gaze took in the stone circle built by men and women thousands of years before the forest was planted. It was amongst these stones that human figures moved quietly in the flickering light of several candles.

Rhea Bradbury shivered slightly, the white, flimsy slip-like shift she was wearing, clinging to her attractive 35 year old body. Midsummer Eve. Even summer nights generally tended to have a chill about them and she was glad a few bottles of red wine would be consumed in a short while, to help raise spirits in more ways than one.

Oddly, she felt she was being watched. She gazed about her, seeing only the group she knew so well. Frank Fletcher was there putting lit candles on alternate stone tops and he had checked the access path through the trees an hour before, to see no-one was about.

Rhea shrugged. Natural enough to feel "watched" in a dark forest. She smiled to herself. She had already planned her usual Midsummer Day to be peaceful. She always lit her grate fire and took a live coal from it twixt ten and twelve o'clock, to bury secretly in the garden without saying a word to anyone. That brings good luck all year.

Rhea had never married. Content with her life in a tiny two up and two down cottage with its bathroom extension and a conservatory filled with plants, she painted wildlife and illustrated children's books. Her cottage garden filled with flowers, herbs and three apple trees was her pride and joy, her "work" for healing as a White or HedgeWitch, proving helpful to many folk and wild creatures over several years.

Rhea preferred to simply call herself a witch, or at most a hedge witch, someone in tune with nature, prepared to help others via "the old ways". "White" wasn't necessary she felt but as there were still a few who used the craft to better themselves or even in a harmful manner the terms "black" and "white" magic were meaningful to some.

As a hedge witch she followed the craft as a solitary all year round with the exception of meeting a few other witches at important days of the year such as this very night.

She remembered her maternal grandmother in Wales, where she had spent her youth, making clay "midsummer men" and putting bits of valerian in them for love divination. She chuckled aloud as she recalled how her own attempt to prophesy whether she and a current boyfriend, a policeman, would wed, and the two "midsummer men" had leaned apart by next morning. That was that. Rhea had felt relief and the policeman boyfriend had been promoted to Bristol. If he could see me now, she thought, looking down at her scantily clad body and long, naked legs. She chuckled again happily.

"You alright Rhea?" Jayne, a similarly clad young woman who ran an antiques business from a small Dartmoor town, asked her. "You seem jolly tonight. Secret joke?"

"Just a bit of nostalgia Jayne. But eager to get started. Time to call everyone to their places."

She walked to the Keystone of the Fernworthy Circle, clapping her hands together gently. A hush fell on the assembled group of nine, five women and four men. Rhea raised both hands skywards and said, "Let the spirits of the forest, of the air, water and earth join us on this Midsummer's Eve".

It was the last words she was to utter for a while.

With a snarling roar Merlin launched himself from the trees, landing in a crouching hunched coil of muscle power and raking claws as he swept his right forepaw in a wide arc, baring his gleaming fangs in the candlelit glow.

"Aargh!" the roar came again, ending in a coughing grunt, then he charged, a black hurtling demon of the night, to run out of the circle of gaping humans.

Rhea, transfixed, saw Jayne Hooper fall sideways onto the grass as the huge black animal dashed into the darkness, to disappear without further sound.

"My God! Are you alright Jane?" One of the men clad in a white cowled robe bent over the half naked, prostrate form, lifting her gently by the shoulders.

Rhea ran across, seeing Jayne's eyes flicker open.

"You must have fainted Jayne. Good grief! I thought we'd invoked some huge fearsome spirit. Almost wet myself." She tried to laugh but the sound would not come.

The man who had reached Jayne first lifted her to her feet and she held on to a standing stone. The group drew close about her, faces showing fear and alarm.

"We had better get out of here Rhea. We'll each take a candle and our torches and I'll go first along the path. Let's hope whatever it was has gone. I expect it was as frightened as we were."

John Armitage, a local smallholder, turned on the beam of his powerful torch and swept it around in a wide circle.

Nothing stirred amongst the trees.

"I doubt if it's anything like as frightened as me. That almost gave me a heart attack."

Jack Barrow, who worked at a tourist holiday complex on the moor shuddered. "But John's right. Back to the cars, lock the doors and get out of here. I think our Midsummer's Eve ended three minutes ago."

Rhea looked around the stone circle. Once again she knew she was being watched, they were all being watched. Her earlier instincts had been right. The hairs on her neck bristled. In the light from the torches and candles she glanced upwards and her heart missed a beat. High in a tree two glowing eyes glared down from a dark crouching shape blacker than the night. She looked away quickly.

"Yes. Let's all go back to my place and drink those bottles of red wine. I've some snacks there and though it's small we can just sit anywhere."

"Thanks Rhea", Jayne said. "My legs 'll work ok now. What a story and none of us can tell it."

"No. I'm glad too. If the animal had meant harm we couldn't have done a thing about it."

The subdued group, they never bothered to call themselves a coven, trooped in single file along the track out of the forest leaving darkness to fall about the ancient stone circle.

Merlin lay on his tree platform, his great cat's eyes adjusting to what light there was filtering from a now moonlit sky. He had reacted to fire and people in darkness born of some deep rooted impulse or instinct from the past. Now he felt again the peace of the forest.

14

Leaving Dartmoor

MERLIN padded along a moonlit Dartmoor lane lined with tall foxgloves, and dandelions growing on a steep earth and grass bank on one side and an old dry stone, lichen covered wall on the other. Rowan, hawthorn and gorse topped the stone wall, growing from the field edge it retained. He had left Fernworthy two days before, disturbed from his lair by too many people being about and with a last meal there, of roe deer, he had moved away under cover of darkness.

His route took him northwards to Kes Tor which he climbed to view the terrain, drinking from a rain water filled rock basin near the summit. By nightfall on the first night of his journeying he had passed Gidleigh and reached a place called Throwleigh, still moving northerly under the moon. But Gidleigh's Doll Castle and Throwleigh Church's old bench ends held no interest for a big-cat. Here two late travelling cyclists, seeing him in the beams of their cycle lights, had braked hard, both falling off their machines to watch staring and fearful as the big-cat trotted close by them. Merlin paid them no heed, intent upon his own journeying though he knew not where he was heading.

Merlin moved on across the moor. Unknown to him Rhea Bradbury had gone back to the Fernworthy stone circle, to kneel and say a prayer for his safe-keeping. In doing so she found a large polished button of horn and an old urn containing a flint knife. Deeply moved she took the items home to her cottage and made a note in her diary that they came from the black leopard of Dartmoor on Midsummer's Eve.

Merlin found the Taw river again, killing a rat and eating it whole by a waterfall with pools of moonlight washing tree roots. He struck a trout in a shallow pool and ate it, his first taste of raw, fresh fish and on he went following the river. Sleeping sheep awoke to raise weary heads, watching the dark shadowy shape pass them by, and fell asleep again. He stepped on a sleeping snipe that squawked a tired protest and lay with open wings on its four broken eggs, once pear shaped and beautiful.

Merlin moved on. He had not seen the snipe in the dark sedge tussock. She would lay a second clutch to replace the first and would not remember the gasping cry she had uttered when stepped on by the big-cat. She moved to one side of the broken eggs and being a bird of the day, fell swiftly asleep once more.

When Merlin was a mile away a hedgehog on its nocturnal rambles, made a meal of the snipe eggs then sniffing briefly at the sleeping snipe it went on its way.

Merlin's ground swallowing strides ate distance, a black shadow following flashing white water and he was soon at Green Taw where an otter suddenly stood very still as the big-cat padded gruntingly by. When he had moved on she slipped into the river close by a bridge of stone, washing away the sudden shock of seeing the leopard. She clambered into her holt after shaking her coat free of water and suckled her three cubs born with the new moon's rising.

Her mate watched Merlin pass a quarter of a mile further downstream where he was eating a brown trout caught moments before in a pool on the widening Taw. A glance at the cat and the otter continued eating hungrily, crunching and chewing meat and bones. Later only the head and tail, joined by a bony spinal cord, was left and within the hour that was eaten by a foraging brown rat.

Merlin loped on tirelessly. He saw tiny green eyes reflecting the moonlight where a family of stoats were hunting rabbits, then passed a badger drinking from the river beneath stunted rowans and thorns. He could hear the squeaks of mice. Once the cat like call of a little owl perched on the stone wall of a cottage had him pause, then on he went seeing the first silver sliver of the dawn in the eastern sky.

Daylight on its way. A Dutch barn at a field edge. Merlin was well away from the wilder moor now and in farming country. Cautiously he sniffed about the barn which, full of hay, smelt sweet. A cockerel crowed to the first light and Merlin leapt up high into the hay, turned a few times, washed carefully until his coat gleamed, then curling up he fell asleep with his tail around his nose.

15

Taw Valley

MERLIN lay quietly dozing in a stand of tall pines planted on a steep hillside. He lay across the top of a log pile that had been made from three of the pines when they had been felled. All about at the edge of the stand of trees were purple rhododendrons and many azaleas, blooming with a profusion of orange, pink, red and white. These edged a long area of grassland with a few sand pits.

Merlin had killed and eaten from a muntjac deer which had come too close, with four others of its kind as the leopard was crossing a golf course, and with a full belly he had taken the remains of the carcase to drop it by the log pile, and he had slept

It was Merlin's first encounter with muntjac deer and his prey had been rubbing its forehead on a tree and on the ground, to leave scent as a territory mark. The buck had not seen the big cat and when rushed had had no time to flee or even to bring its own finely pointed fang-like teeth to bear against the leopard. Fully grown it was, however, only eighteen inches at the shoulder and had only recently begun growing its antlers again after casting them in May.

The others in the group had scattered at Merlin's charge and were now together a half mile away from the golf course, feeding on yew and brambles in a churchyard. Muntjac may feed at any time of day though they favour dusk time for their browsing, and as they have no fixed breeding season the does may give birth every seven or eight months, thus the species is slowly but gradually spreading into and across the Westcountry.

Merlin roused for he could hear human voices. Through the dense azalea vegetation he could see two people standing on the grass sward. Then the voices ceased and Merlin

It was Merlin's first encounter with a Muntjac deer.

heard a "thwack" and suddenly a white, round object struck the grass before him to roll to a stop close by.

Then another "thwack" sounded and as the leopard moved forward to the edge of the neatly mown golf fairway he was struck very forcefully above one eye by a hard object which rolled onto the grass before him.

Merlin roared, more from the sudden shock than pain and he raced out onto the grass to stare at the two humans standing still many yards away. Some instinct told him the missile had been caused by them and he trotted towards them, fangs bared, seeing the two men turn and take to their heels.

Merlin broke into a gallop but seeing them reach four other humans he ran in an arc to avoid them. Passing sheds where other humans were standing, pointing, he increased his speed and leaping a tall fence he loped easily along a tree lined lane to find himself at a farmstead where he squeezed between old gorse stems. Here he laid, peaceful once again as linnets fed five nestlings nearby.

Through half closed eyes he watched a group of green hairstreak butterflies perching on vantage points amongst the gorse, or chasing each other in short bursts of swift flight. Eggs laid earlier in the summer had hatched and the gorse was busy with many insects. Merlin slept to the sound of bees humming and the occasional popping of gorse seed pods heated by the hot summer sun.

16

Investigations

NEIL Harvey was a police sergeant who had volunteered along with many other members of the force to be a Wildlife Liaison Officer. It was an extra duty, the designation not as yet part of the police system that allowed for a separate department. Thus the WLOs as they became known were officers interested in wildlife generally, and aware of the often horrendous crimes committed against creatures other than humans, but certainly by humans.

The general public soon became aware of the Wildlife Liaison set- up and thus it was to Neil Harvey and officers like him that many big-cat sightings were reported even though no crimes were involved as such. Soon the title of Wildlife Liaison Officer became Wildlife Crime Officer, a more apt sounding name and it was learned that wildlife crime globally was second only to drugs in terms of the huge sums of money involved.

Thus it was that on a day when mist hung heavy on the landscape Sergeant Harvey found himself investigating sheep kills on a farm, kills that had been attributed to a big-cat or cats.

Two fully grown ewes had been killed and two others maimed to an extent they had had to be put down. Tracks at a farm gate were found and a local naturalist had been called in to help identify them.

The policeman, the farmer and his wife stood huddled by the carcases, covered now with a tarpaulin, as the naturalist strolled towards them from the gateway where the footprints had been found.

"Dog kill", he said amiably. "And dog tracks. Big dog mind, well, big paws anyway. Do you want a cast taken of them?" He looked at the policeman.

"May as well. And that confirms it's most likely a dog or dogs killed the sheep, as I thought", the officer replied.

"Oh it's definite. That isn't a big-cat kill at all."

"Well, a big black cat has been seen on the farm and somebody saw one ripping open bin bags down in the pub car park for food." The farmer looked at his wife, who nodded.

"Saw'n myself Sergeant. Up in our top meadow. No sheep up there tis true but he or she was big, as big as our sheep dogs easy, with a long tail, good yard long that tail. Twas a cat alright. True it took no notice of me. Went through the hedge into the lane. That was a'past two yesterday afternoon."

"Did you see which way it went Mrs. Green?" The sergeant asked.

"No. As I said to Bill when I got home. I wasn' going to chase after an animal like that in case it turned on me. Then we found the sheep this morning and phoned the vet' and the police."

"A cat ripping open bin bags when there are scores of sheep everywhere, and lots of rabbits, suggests the cat is no sheep killer Neil", the naturalist said. And anyway I'd stake my reputation on this being a dog related incident."

"OK Tom. Must agree with you on that, and the vet's said much the same. So we have a big-cat about, and sheep killing dogs, or one dog. Great. That adds interest to my job."

He chuckled.

"Kettle's on. Do have a cup of tea before you go. This mist's going to turn to rain so warm up beforehand."

The four wandered down to the white painted farm house.

"Forecast says dry for the next two days Mrs. Green", the sergeant said.

"Anne. Call me Anne. Well tis going to rain, mark my words. Certainly round here it is, that's right isn't it Bill?"

Bill Green chuckled. "Yes, it'll rain within the hour. Specially if the forecast says "dry". They get a few wrong

MERLIN

these days. Course localised weather round here. I've been up in top field in sunshine watching it raining over cross the valley. Come and have a mug of Anne's tea and a bit of that fruit cake too."

"I'd better way get the casts of the prints done Neil, and a photo or two, if rain's coming or they'll be gone. But not before a taste of that cake. It looks ansome."

Bill said "Tastes even better than it looks chaps. Tuck in. Anne's a lovely cook, look at my equator". He patted his stomach appreciatively.

Snack over, Tom took his leave of the others and fetched a knapsack from his car boot, checking to see he'd got enough Plaster of Paris and his bottle of water, spoon and pastry cutter which he used to contain the cast mixture from running everywhere. He grinned as he thought of Anne Green's delightful cooking and his own use of similar utensils.

As he trudged back to the gateway he paused to watch a robin feeding its young in a hedgebank nest. The little bird had worms in its beak, tiny worms and he marvelled at how they found a constant supply when such "food" was virtually invisible to the human eye.

A pair of blue tits were feeding young in a nestbox about ten feet up in an oak and he noticed the mist was thickening, swirling densely white across the fields.

At the gateway he knelt and prepared his mixture, pouring it as a thick creamy substance into the pastry cutter already in place as a surround to the best of the dog footprints, the large claw marks clearly visible.

A sound made him glance up, but seeing nothing he waited for the Plaster of Paris to harden, which took only a few minutes. Leaning down to pick up the case he again heard a sound and knew it was the panting of a large animal. Tom gazed intently into a stand of gorse some thirty feet away. He thought he could see movement, thought he could hear a low growl but the mist swirled whiter and the first patter of raindrops tapped his shoulders.

Gathering up his bits and pieces Tom rose. He took two

quick flashlit photographs of the prints putting an old wooden six inch rule beside them, then he turned and hurried back to the farmhouse and his car.

Bill Green stood waiting. "Well, everything alright? Get what you wanted? Anne was right about the rain. Can you drink another cuppa?"

"No thanks Bill. Neil's gone I see. I'll let you all see this stuff in a few days. Thanks for your hospitality, it has been a useful visit, I've enjoyed it. Well, not the sheep kills of course but I am sure it's a rogue dog thing. See you soon."

Tom got into his car and drove off, the rain now beating hard on the windscreen.

In the lane, hidden by an eight foot tall stand of gorse, long ago used as fodder and fuel on the farm, stood a ramshackle galvanised iron roofed shed with no door. Inside, two lurchers rested from the rain, large "crosses" with grey and grizzled faces and coats and an ancestry that included greyhound and wolfhound.

For five years they had been owned and well looked after by a Welshman who had moved to Somerset to live after retiring from hill farming early due to a weak heart. Each day the two lurchers were taken out across the Somerset Levels to catch rabbits for their own food and occasionally for their owner who was partial to rabbit stews and pies washed down by good, rough cider.

On a morning six weeks before the sheep kills at the Green's farm the two dogs had found their owner dead in his arm chair by a dying log fire and their barking and howling had brought the nearest neighbour to the door. He knew the man was dead but could not get by the dogs guarding their beloved master as the police and doctor were called. Then came a dog warden and his colleague armed with noosed poles. They had been struck to the ground by the two charging lurchers who had dashed into the road past officials and bystanders to flee into the wilds of Somerset. No longer owned, no longer wanted the two had remained together, brother lurchers, becoming part of the statistics of dogs thrown out or lost that increases day by day as a very British phenomenon.

The lurchers fed well on rabbits and other wild animals as they moved from Somerset into Devon's Exmoor, harassed by various humans who didn't want them about. They reached the outskirts of the town close by the Green's farm in the early hours of a morning and suddenly frightened by a vehicle being driven to deliver milk, chugging out of the darkness, the two ran into the garden of a house, to hide in a greenhouse with its door swinging open.

That same morning a gust of wind blew the greenhouse door shut, trapping the two lurchers inside. At daybreak they had nudged and scratched at the door in an effort to escape but it served only to force the door tighter shut. The lurchers lay dozing, waiting for someone to come into the garden but no-one came and they slept hungry into the night.

On the next day the dogs ate a mouse each, caught scampering along a row of plant pots but their hunger and thirst worsened. Still no-one came, the dogs sleeping a second night through in the greenhouse trap.

Then on the afternoon of the third day they heard human voices and after a while three people came into the garden.

"Well as you see, the garden is also well maintained with the shed and that greenhouse is fairly new. I'm sure it is a large enough garden to serve both your needs as keen gardeners and of course, vacant possession means a quick arrangement if the house suits."

The estate agent pointed to the greenhouse, saying he believed it was kept unlocked for viewers.

The three strolled to the door to the sudden barking of the two trapped lurchers, the startled estate agent opening the door to be bowled over by the freed dogs charging by him.

"Good grief! Whose are they?" he shouted. "They weren't there last Saturday when I came round. Who'd keep two dogs in somebody elses greenhouse?"

But the lurchers were gone. Over the garden wall and

into a quiet lane adjoining woods they raced, running as one at a speed few other dogs could match.

It was thus, starving and thirsty they had reached Green's farm and totally out of character, charged into a flock of sheep in a frenzy of hunger. One ewe had lowered her head, running straight at the dogs, bowling one somersaulting into an old stone trough, to find the other at her face and so the battle and carnage had ensued.

Strangely after the first brief but bloody moments the two dogs suddenly ceased their attack yet eating nothing from the carcases, had leapt back into the lane where both killed and ate rats scurrying along the farm lane. They drank rain-water from a half barrel discovered by the old shed, wandered in and fell asleep exhausted but no longer hungry.

Merlin's own passing through Green's farm had been just that. The only signs he had left of his presence was urine sprayed on the gateway into top meadow for he, too had eaten two rats caught in the hay and left no evidence of such kills.

The two lurchers left the farm when the rain ceased, their paws leaving no prints as they crossed fields, lanes and roads to reach a small seaside village. Here in a cottage beside the village church they were welcomed and fed by a couple who had recently lost their own dog to old age.

"No collars. They be strays Bessie. But look how they respond to some tlc, and good grub."

"You'm right dear. Nice looking faces too. Straight by the fire place too. They had a good home once, I dare say. Well we've got spare collars Sam. Let's keep them, what do you reckon?"

Sam looked at this wife and at the two lurchers already asleep sprawled together by the fire's glowing embers.

"Seems to me us ev been adopted Bessie. Yes, I'm all for it, I do miss our old Bramble. Yes, tis fate is how I sees it. Us be a family of four then Bessie." He chuckled happily.

Bessie smiled, resuming her knitting. She too had ached terribly at the loss of Bramble and other dogs they'd owned.

Five graves in the large garden, adjoining the churchyard with its own gravestones, were testimony to their love of dogs.

"We'll call them Bill and Ben, shall we dear?" she said.

"From little flowerpots, they've growed. Yes, alright, Bill and Ben. Straight from the greenhouse." Sam puffed at his pipeful of shag tobacco, never to know how right he was.

17

Homeward Bound

MERLIN was crossing a large open field with ditches around three of its edges, one formed by a disused railway embankment. Here dragonflies and damselflies zoomed by day, some emerging from nymph cases at night to hang waiting for a drying sun to rise.

It was a night with no moon, but starlit and the big-cat had left Dartmoor far behind him. He paused hearing grunting and the sound of stones and soil falling, then movement beneath a lone hawthorn tree caught his attention. An animal was digging furiously and so intent upon its activity it was unaware of Merlin's stealthy approach. The leopard had seen badgers many times in his journeying but not close to and he stood now within feet of the digging mustelid.

Some sixth sense inherent in all wild animals, in our domestic animals and livestock, but mostly lost to modern humans caused the badger to suddenly cease its digging and whirl about to face whatever had stimulated that sense. The badger was an elderly sow who had borne several litters in the nearby sett and was known by her kin for her matriarchal loyalty. But she was also short tempered as well as short sighted and now she bristled at the large, dark shape before her, her still sharp ears and nose testing the air, her very sharp claws ready to do battle.

Merlin stared at her, more puzzled than angry. He could smell rabbit but did not know the badger was in the act of digging out a litter of rabbit kittens to eat, for their sweet meat to her was even tastier than earthworms, and more filling.

The badger recognised the huge size of the leopard, knowing instinctively it was a predator and not an animal of the usual cattle and sheep kind she oft times met with in the fields all about. But she had fought off a few dogs in her time and now she stood her ground, grunting, snarling, baring her own fangs and ready to defend herself to the last, as is the way of badgers.

Merlin stared long and hard at the bristling badger before him. It was not food. He was not even hungry. He turned away and wandered on, leaving the field through a gap in the hawthorn hedge where sheep often broke through to wander a mile or more of saltings by a tidal river.

Merlin had again found the Taw he had splashed in at Dartmoor's Belstone many days before. He passed a vixen eating a black headed gull that roosted beside the river in the darkness of night. The fox had learned many gulls, waders and duck roosted here and she had made her earth in a bramble covered earth bank close by the rabbit burrows.

The leopard did not pause, moving on to come to hills of soil and rubble and rows of small buildings that smelled of humans. He could hear the creaking of huge machines lying waiting for the day when they would suddenly come alive with use, to continue to build a vast bridge across the river. Merlin paused. He had arrived at a huge mound of large stones where a flock of more than five hundred Canada Geese drifted, honking gently to one another.

Merlin stared across the stones into the distance, hearing the sighing and clanking of wind buffeted machinery, jumping to one side as a bright object rolled across his path. It was a yellow plastic hard hat dropped by its workman owner as he lit a cigarette and watched the first flurry of rain ripple the river about the geese flock.

The man noted where his safety hat came to rest, beginning to clamber down over the rubble pile to retrieve it. He saw, too, the movement as a large black shape jumped to avoid it and crouching he knew he was looking at a big cat.

"Strewth, a panther", he murmured to himself and then rose to his feet as the animal moved out across the temporary bridge of stones, to vanish into the shadows. Turning he went back to his caravan lodging, one of several housing

Merlin stared long and hard at the bristling badger before him.

workmen on the new bridge construction, to sit looking out of a window at the first glimmer of daylight reflecting on the river. He grinned as he thought of his wife's expression when he told her of his week, and of seeing a panther just a few yards away, when he went home for the weekend.

Oh yes, she'd say. The lager's a bit strong down in North Devon then.

Merlin began to run, his great ground covering strides taking him by houses whose rooftops now glistened with gently falling rain. Lights were beginning to come on as people struggled out of bed to face another day. The cat crossed a road and grass bank, then another road to leave the dual carriageway behind as he dropped into a field which stretched up before him, topped by an old folly.

He loped on up over wet grass, hearing the dawn chorus of many birds as he reached the stone folly, to follow a lane to a village roadway. Now Merlin knew where he was. Crossing the shining blackness of the tarmac road he trotted along another lane by a stream, then up by a former mill where a dog barked furiously at his passing.

More fields, then trees as he reached familiar woods and old territory. He sprayed the stile leading into the woods to follow a track up to a high bank with his old cave where soil and stones had long since fallen away down the steep wood slope. Merlin went inside, lying with his great black head on his forepaws, watching the rain nod the flowers of yellow wood avens and wood spurge just before his nose, then he sighed, and slept...

18

Of Poachers

FREDDIE Lakeman was a "jobber". He was also a poacher. Thus if you wanted your garden sorted out, a hedge layed, or a fresh salmon or pheasant, Fred was your man. Locals knew him as "Laker". Locals have a way of name tagging a person with some people unaware of how they are known to others. Some names were very amusing, even a touch rude. The retired grocer who was called Oates, renowned for his miserly ways, was "Tight-arse", pinched from Titus Oates. The doctor who had a skull on his desk, presumably to remind patients things could get worse, was known as Hamlet.

The more popular one was with the villagers of Beccott, the more polite the local nick-name. So "Laker" Lakeman it was, a local man born and bred of an Irish father and a Devonshire mother, at the edge of the town. That was another thing, the "locals" and "furriners", the latter meaning 25 years minimum to be fully accepted whether they paid well for a service or not. Even then much depended on their attitude and if it was known one such referred to having a "little man who comes in" to do this or that, the "little man" would do one job and make another for later.

"Laker" was a lurcher man and good to his dog, though it had to work for its living. He'd always had lurchers, lean, tough and fast, though once indoors they know how to relax and enjoy a snooze, as do most dogs.

It was a still, dark night and "Laker" who admitted to "knocking 40" had parked his red van by the village church which was close to the local inn. He was now heading silently along an old, little used lane, his dog Jasper following tight on his heels. A tawny owl hooted and the sound of water running in the ditch below the two, told of the several springs issuing from the rock here.

Occasionally "Laker" shone a powerful torch to check the way, holding fingers over the beam to diffuse it. He did not want landowners knowing he was about even though the lane was a public footpath. He had one or two "orders" for salmon and pheasant and the autumn run was on for the king of fish. He preferred trout himself, and the bass and flounder caught in the big river, but salmon at the weir were easy pickings.

"Laker" kept a few snares and a gaff in a derelict barn with a rickety loft. You did not carry your gear about the countryside, you left them in sensible places en route to your quarry, whether that quarry was salmon, trout, pheasant or whatever. Not that "Laker" was a mercenary poacher. He was of the old school, food for the table, and maybe a few quid for more food for the table. And his dog. They both had to eat.

He chuckled as he reached the lane bottom. Many's the copper, he thought, who took his wife out to an evening meal of meats poached in the area and sold at the back door of the inn where they ate. Eating the evidence. He chuckled again and moved on across a field below dark woods, hearing the distant roar of water over the weir.

In the dim light cast by a half moon "Laker" could see the old barn surrounded by brambles beneath tall, straggling hawthorns in the hedgerow. Once there had been stately elm trees along the hedge, wonderful trees, but they had become stricken by Dutch Elm disease and were now stumps where the farmer's chain saw had felled them as dead giants. Victims of too many vehicles, "Laker" called the trees, the disease having spread from road sides into deeper countryside.

"Go on boy", he whispered to his lurcher companion. "Go on Jasper."

He watched the tall, leggy lurcher leave his side, its speckled coat grey in the moonlight, just a shadow as it moved lithely towards the old barn to see if all was safe and quiet.

"Laker" stood watching, as he always stood, admiring the dog's silent, obedient lope forwards and then Jasper stopped in his tracks.

"Laker" watched, puzzled The lurcher was some 50 yards from the barn. From the woods came the sharp "kee-wick" of a tawny owl. He felt the breeze stir about his face, knowing Jasper was raising his head to sniff and smell the tales carried by the breeze. The dog remained still. "Laker" gave a low whistle, a sound known only to the dog. Within seconds it was about and by his side, noble head pointing at the old barn. "Laker" put his hand down.

"Good boy", he whispered, then froze. The lurcher was shaking violently. It was afraid. "Laker" felt a tingle go through his own body. Jasper was afraid of nothing. No more was he, yet tonight "Laker" was very uneasy. The farmer? No. He would not bother to lie in wait for poachers of a late night time. The Police? No. Where had they parked? Laker had come to the barn via the shortest route and anyway he and his dog were, technically, on a public path no matter how obscure, no matter what the time of day. Other poachers? No. Where were they parked? And why hide in the barn?

Jasper whined. Unusual. Unheard of. The dog still shook. "Laker" considered the possibility of someone living rough in the barn. It made sense. But that would not have Jasper shaking. He'd be ready to go in and tear trouser legs at a flash. The breeze swiftened on "Laker's" face and Jasper whined again, turned and went behind his legs, standing pointing at the barn. Then the dog whined again, an almost despairing sound.

This was getting nowhere "Laker" thought. There were salmon to obtain and he needed to go into the barn to collect his gaff.

"C'mon boy", he whispered to his dog.

The dog did not move. He still shivered beneath Laker's hand, but the night was not cold.

Laker was uneasy. He felt pulled about by different alarms. All his poaching instincts were alert and cunning on the one hand but a portion of his own mind began to cause him to tremble ever so slightly. Like his dog, Laker felt rather than knew that something was very wrong. Could he hear the sound of footsteps? Of breathing? No, surely it was the usual rustle of breeze stirred leaves.

Surely, Laker thought, they were alone. He wanted to chuckle but couldn't. He wanted to turn around to peer into the almost darkness. Why don't I just turn around? He thought he could feel a presence and felt silly. He, Laker, hardy and not afraid of the night country. Shadows about the barn moved like faceless beings. Laker had imagination. It had saved his bacon many times.

The moon showed suddenly from above the trees, a half moon with a wide halo. Rain on the way soon. And Laker suddenly saw the barn door was half open. He could see the wooden plank door half ajar, and the pitch black darkness of the interior. Was that a darker shadow in the darkness? He felt the dog nudge his leg, then it whined again and took a step backwards.

For the first time a real qualm came over him, followed by a definite feeling of weakness of the joints as Laker realised he was experiencing fear. He knew he must resist and overcome the feeling, knowing it would transmit to the lurcher. That was it. Jasper's strange attitude, his seeming fear, was entering him also.

He stepped forward a pace and as he did so a coughing grunt reached his ears from the direction of the barn door.

Surely, Laker thought, the fool of a farmer hadn't put a bull in the field, and left the barn open for it. Surely not in a field with a right of way across it. Surely, he thought, those are two eyes glinting in the doorway, catching the moonlight, and too low down for a bull. Low enough for a sheep. Or dog. Or...

Merlin stepped from the barn into the almost dark night. He was hungry. He had been sat on his haunches for too long, feeling the draught, watching the human and the dog, watching for them to go away. He had seen the man step forward, the dog remaining still and he had stepped out to

Was that a darker shadow in the darkness?

not be trapped or shut in by humans.

Merlin was hungry and annoyed. He snarled a warning, seeing the human and the dog turn and run. Merlin roared, then snarling he trotted after the two.

"Go boy!" Laker's words of command spurred the lurcher to swiftly reach a five barred gate and leap it with ease as his master threw himself up and over the top bar to sprawl in a heap on the other side.

They were in the lane and the lane was dark with many shadows. Laker felt real fear. For all he knew every shadow was another big-cat. For all he knew every tree held another on its lower branches, swiping with talons to rip him asunder. Laker sent the torch beam piercing the night, seeing his lurcher racing ahead. He almost laughed hysterically, realising he was not going to look back in case the animal was at his heels. He ran faster.

In the van again, doors locked and with Jasper by his side, he flung his arms about the lurcher as they both regained their breath and composure. Laker shone the torch along the lane. Nothing moved. He shivered once.

"Somebody's walked over me grave Jasper", he said.

To the local inn, or home? He decided home, with locked doors, a poke or two at the log fire, a treat for Jasper and a hot whisky toddy. No salmon. And he was not going back to the barn in a hurry either. Not until he knew more about the cat. Freddie Lakeman's got a lot of living to do yet, he thought, as he drove homeward.

"That was a cat and a half wad'n it boy", he said to his lurcher, "it really was some cat."

A mile away Merlin struck a hen pheasant from her nest. He ate the nine eggs in the hedgerow nest, ignoring the startled "kok-kok of the cock pheasant roosting on a branch above him. He gripped the hen bird in his powerful jaws, followed a hare path through the hedge and took the plump prey back to the barn for supper.

19

Home Wood

MERLIN was in a bad mood. He was hungry. It had rained heavily for six days with barely any respite. Most of the creatures he would normally have caught as food were hidden from the weather and making only brief forays twixt the heavy rain showers in order to eat and survive.

As with all leopards, Merlin would eat almost anything. All his needs were involved with food and shelter, the heavily featured land of the Westcountry providing well for such needs. Though leopards are carnivores they eat fruit as well as meat. Even insects are taken and animals from mice size to, in their native countries, gnu and antelopes, even cheetahs. Thus Merlin found his British territory provided adequate wild food. He avoided sheep and cattle, finding it easy to obtain food of the wild kind though his former owner had fed him with beef and mutton times enough.

Merlin looked out from his lair, smelling the air, the scent of honeysuckle strong to his sensitive nose, the plant giving out its sweet smell the better after rain. Here it grew in profusion over the hawthorn and hazel of the hedgebank which roofed his lair, binding the wood, the lovely woodbine as country folk called it.

A deep-throated growl rumbled in Merlin's chest and throat. He reached out a paw, touching the mud before him. He did not like wet and mud but no rain was falling, that which he could hear being the pattering of rain drops from water laden branches and leaves.

Shafts of late sunlight broke through the clouds and tree branches, the first for almost a week and immediately steam arose from gates and hedgerows, forming different clouds as Merlin stepped from his lair and roared. The sound reverberated through the woodland, causing several wood

pigeons to wing skywards, causing a shiver to run through
the body of the fox that lived in an earth at the far side of
the woods.

He padded out from the woods, crossing a steep field with
a smaller woodland at its bottom and pausing to drink from
a rainwater pool he watched the movement of a male brim-
stone butterfly emerging from ivy growing up an oak tree.
Primroses grew along the bank separating the field and
trees, the latter left as cover for foxes and pheasants by
hunting landowners who also liked to see wildlife on their
land.

Merlin moved on, reaching conifer woods with drier
ground beneath the unbrashed trees which he liked. He
moved faster, hunger driving him forward, to reach a clearing where lay the hooved legs of deer and the skulls of three
hinds. He snarled, smelling humans, moving on from this
place where poachers worked on red deer carcases before
taking away the venison to their buyers.

Minutes later he emerged at the forestry edge to gaze
down upon farm buildings and the blue smoke of a fire
issuing from the chimney of one of these. The cat could see
water glints from a large pond and a number of large white
birds grouped at the water's edge by a stone wall. He roared
again, the sound ending with the coughing grunt of his
kind as he trotted downhill along a vehicle track leading to
the farm road. A farm collie began barking incessantly,
facing the sound as the farmer stood thoughtfully watching
his fields, wondering at his dog's obvious excitement. And
when the collie, one of the hardiest and skilled as a sheepdog for miles around, ceased barking and moved behind his
legs the farmer felt unease.

All was silent now save for the drip-drip of raindrops, a
different sound the farmer thought, than the patter of
actual rain, as if the life had gone out of it. He bent to move
an upturned metal bucket, disliking the constant drumming
sound and as he straightened up a black shadow moved
across the yard between two outbuildings. He felt his dog
move round his legs to stand in front of him, growling low

but there was a hint of a whimper in the sound.

"Stay Ben." He heard himself giving a low command to the dog. He knew it was afraid but was moved knowing it would defend him to the last. True courage that was.

"Come Ben." He backed away and opening the farm-house door he went indoors with the dog to sit by the last embers of a log fire. His wife looked up from her "People's Friend" magazine, a weekly treat away from TV.

"Everything alright John?" she asked smiling.

"Aye. Fox about I expect. Ben gets in a tizz sometimes." He smiled back at his wife and patted Ben on the head. He knew the shadowy figure he had seen was no fox and had locked the door and bolted it before sitting down.

Sundown. Night fell swiftly on cloudy days, no slow observable sunset as on clearer days.

Merlin crossed silently between the two farm buildings, hearing the dog's growl and his master's voice. As he passed along the outer wall of the second building he could clearly hear the farm door open and close, a sound familiar to his ears from former captive days.

Six white geese slept in an outhouse, a lean-to affair against the bigger barn. Merlin killed one of these and was thirty yards away with his prize before the others awoke to chase him from farmyard to field then they stood watching his departing black shadow carrying their now dead companion.

The farmer heard their calls and quietened his collie who had run, hackles raised, to nose at the bottom of the farm door.

"There Mary, the geese will have seen the fox off sure enough. Let's get a bit further with this yer book I'm reading. Oddly enough tis about a fox as you know, "Old Red", by that local chap."

He settled back to read, Ben the sheepdog lying at his feet as a mile away Merlin ate his fill of the plump goose and viewed the night contentedly.

In the distance thunder rumbled. "Perhaps that is what upset Ben, John", Mary said.

"P'raps you'm right dear", murmured her husband.

Next morning he counted five white geese by the pond, finding large cat paw prints in the mud which he stepped in to obliterate. Later by the pond he saw a heron take one of the large fish he had stocked it with a couple of years before. He chuckled. Not much different about the two predators really, wild poachers in a way but unlike human poachers, simply living in the wild and having to hunt for food.

Swallows suddenly appeared, flying low, dipping for water and insects over the surface of the pond and he watched a red admiral butterfly fly from hibernation in the hay barn, the first of the year.

"Tis going to be an interesting year Ben", he muttered. "Come on boy, let's go in to breakfast."

20

On the Farm

THE harsh chattering of magpies awoke Merlin as the two birds moved from their domed nest in an oak in the hedgerow by Merlin's old linhay lair. He rose and stretched, leaving claw marks in the linhay doorway, to amble outside into a gold and peach dawn-light. Merlin crouched, hunching his shoulders, pushing his head into soaking grasses as he washed his face in the morning dew.

Seeing him the two magpies flew away down over the steep field to seek breakfast and annoy smaller birds and grey squirrels for it was springtime with many young birds and mammals as well as eggs to be eaten. Seeing the two birds from the kitchen window of a farmhouse a man saluted them superstitiously but grinned, for two magpies also meant "joy". His wife smiled as she put two plates of sausage, eggs and bacon on the table by the window and they sat contentedly opposite one another to eat.

"Pity them magpies don't keep chickens to lay eggs, like we do maid." The man buttered fresh toast as his wife smiled and nodded for her husband had voiced this opinion many times over the years, as a bird lover aware of the toll magpies take on eggs and young at this time of year. But such beautiful birds she reminded herself.

Merlin stood for a moment in the early morning sunshine then sat on bare earth surrounding an ancient standing stone and began his morning preening, beginning with paw licks and rubbing of face and whiskers.

"There he is again John, having his morning wash by the menhir. He likes it up there."

"Ee do at that, maid. I don't mind im up there and ee don't bother the stock. Less trouble than some of they housing estate dugs when they'm out together.

"There he is again, John, having his morning wash by the menhir."

"Yes and I haven't seen that poacher chap about lately. Not that we'd begrudge him a rabbit or pheasant, they are not ours."

John Parminter chewed reflectively on his crispy bacon. "Mmm. This is good tack maid, lovely bit of bacon. Yes, well, the poacher chap's no more harm than that big cat but ee take's liberties leaving his gear in places on our land. Thinks I don't know, silly chap. But ee'd know it if ee walked into that cat in the dark."

He chuckled and tucked into the remains of his breakfast.

"Yes, that he would. Good night watchman for the farm that cat. I expect he eats what the poacher's after."

"Definite", her husband agreed. "They'm in competition right enough. And us too if ee wants a rabbit or pheasant for the pantry like us do sometimes."

"Not at the moment dear. Anyway I don't want you out competing with our cat, he wouldn't understand. Funny thing is I'm sure he's a "he" not a "she". Don't you think so?"

John looked at his wife long and hard but she saw the twinkle in his eyes and waited, smiling inwardly, for his reply.

"Yes, a male I agree. Quiet and handsome. Has to be a bloke."

His wife laughed. "You old bugger. Have another coffee."

They looked at each other with the love of 30 years.

Merlin gazed down at the old farmhouse. He had known and grown to like humans. It was the love of his owner and he felt him close, yet so far away. He padded down across the field, finding the track to the farm door. He could smell the breakfast eaten by the two country folk and some tugging chords in his memory showed him the face of a bearded man who had fed him and stroked him without malice, only with fondness, only with an eagerness to learn more of this powerful predator who was inwardly but a cat, but an animal, needing food, needing a home, as all creatures need.

John and Mary Parminter watched him amble along their

pathway. They reached out and held hands as the huge black cat stared at their window, stared into their very minds, or so it seemed.

"He's lived with people, or someone, no doubt about it maid. It is uncanny but I feel him as well as see him and it gives me the creeps. There you are, as always maid but I feel lonely, I feel that cat's loneliness", he sighed.

"So do I John". Cats are funny animals anyway but I agree this one reaches out or so it seems to me. But we can't do a thing about it, we daren't."

Outside the window now Merlin stared at the two human shapes within. Mostly the glass panes reflected sky and trees but the two people showed distinctly enough and there was a pleasing smell about the house.

Then the sound of a vehicle came suddenly closer and Merlin felt vibrations beneath his feet – he turned to lope into shrubs by the pathway, merging into the shadows as the vehicle came to a standstill. A man alighted from it to come whistling loudly close by him.

John and Mary Parminter watched as the postman passed within feet of the crouching big cat, carrying a large parcel to their front door. They both met him at their porch, full of shelves and Mary's favourite pot plants for "postie" had been a locally born friend of many years.

"Quick coffee Dave and can you take a couple of letters to post please?" Mary asked him, taking the parcel.

"Yes to both Missus P", Dave said cheerfully, "lovely day coming I think."

Merlin watched them disappear into the house. The shrubbery was quiet and secluded but he was hungry. He rose and turning away from the house he strolled up the pathway towards open fields and woods.

Indoors the postman exploded a mouthful of coffee down his uniform shirt front.

"Good grief John! Do you see that? There look, a huge black cat! Blimey Charley! Oh sorry missus." He apologised to Mary for the outburst as they all watched Merlin leave the farm path for wilder countryside.

"All these years I've driven the mail van round these parts and that's the first time I've seen an animal like that. What'll you do about it John?" Dave wiped his shirt front with a cloth Mary handed him.

"Nothing Dave. Ee hasn't bin any trouble to us so I don't want nort said, or crowds of people poking about if ee sees what I mean." He stared meaningfully at the postman.

"Fair enough folks. I do know what you mean. Cor, I must have walked right past it just now. Sends a shiver up my back that does. But I'm still here so no sweat. Made my day. Ansome."

Merlin had already rushed a group of rabbits grazing by an old warren and was now in amongst a stand of horse chestnut trees enjoying fresh meat.

21

Of Ducks and Foxes

JIMMY Nicholls was 18 and a loner. He worked in a sawmill enjoying the hard work, the out-door-ness of it and the huge sheds and timber stacks which always had some wildlife interest. Wildlife was Jimmy's passion, rain or shine and at home, where he lived with his parents he had stacks of books on natural history. He would have loved to be Sir David Attenborough really, or "BB", his favourite author. But he hadn't the scholarship for such ambitions to become reality and contented himself with a job that brought him lodge, books and his new binoculars, and an SLR camera, second hand from a local shop

Jimmy was a tall, wiry young man, lanky and brown as a berry. He exuded shyness and a quiet strength yet kept himself up with the times and spoke his mind when he felt strongly about a subject.

Today was Friday and a long weekend with a Bank Holiday Monday was his to use so Jimmy was very pleased with life. He decided tomorrow he would test his camera with its 300mm zoom lens on some birdlife along his favourite waterway, there were dippers and grey wagtails there, and always dragonflies. Tonight, binoculars and a scout around the stream to see if the dippers and grey wagtails were nesting. And he still had all Sunday and Monday beyond that.

Half an hour from his home, a dawdle down an old pack horse route of a lane, and he was sitting on a fallen log by the stream where he'd played since he was five years old. Across the field in high summer grasses and tall buttercups a young couple lay as young couples do on summer evenings. Jimmy had quite accidentally spotted them as he searched the field and hedgerows for wildlife, and he had quickly swung his binocular away for he was no intruder on such scenes. Not wishing to be considered a Peeping Tom, Jimmy rose silently to walk slowly upstream to where shallows and a small island allowed him to leap across into the next field. Here he strolled to the weir, crossing the stone top of it to leap wet footed into the adjoining woods.

Six mallard swam towards him, four drakes and two ducks. A bit "tame" he thought. They'd probably learned people sometimes meant food and he'd often seen the children from the former mill feeding them. It was shady in the woods and the sun was beginning to dip, throwing long shadows of trees across the path. He made a mental note of times not to attempt photography as he had yet to obtain flash equipment.

The mallard muttered about him then let the water flow take them into the weir pool. Jimmy guessed they would roost on the bank here for the night.

Then "stritt, stritt", the short flight call of a dipper as the stocky white breasted bird sped by him and Jimmy knew he should have a good weekend with binocular and camera. He was able to follow it with his gaze, seeing it perch on a large stone projecting from the water. Focussing his binocular he could now clearly see the dipper bobbing and dipping on its stone perch, then it flew again to go beneath a bridge arch some fifty yards further downstream.

Must change my vantage point, Jimmy decided and rising to his feet he began to make his way to where he could cross the leat without soaking his walking shoes yet again.

It was then that a dark shadow detached itself from the lengthening tree shadows, to move parallel to him down to the weir pool and mallard.

Jimmy froze in his tracks. Instinctively he knew the animal was not a dog. As it crossed the path, evening sunbeams played into the woods, spotlighting the creature and Jimmy could clearly see it was a large black cat with a long, thick tail upcurved at the end almost like a walking stick.

He felt a little sick, his stomach knotting and he was

almost afraid to breathe. He leaned sideways against an oak tree, watching, his pulses racing.

A female mallard quacked noisily, "Kreck, kreck, kreck, kreck", and the black cat paused.

Jimmy wanted to call out to them but knew that was both stupid and dangerous. Then something incongruous occurred and Jimmy's heart beat faster.

At the weir edge appeared a fox, crouching and intent on gaining a supper of duck meat. It had not seen the big-cat which now had its body crouched, large round head poised, its tail held stiffly behind it.

"Kreck, kreck, kreck", the female mallard on the bank had seen the fox shape silhouetted against the sunlight and the fox rushed the six birds, splashing across the shallows of the overgrown leat.

Jimmy saw duck shapes erupting, orange lit water splashed, heard the quacking ducks panic and saw the black cat charge with a roaring, snarling cry into the midst of it all. He felt his stomach lurch and he sank to his knees feeling fear as one male mallard flew low up over the wood, one wing striking his face and another went straight up into the trees. Not daring to move he stared down, every muscle in his body clenched, to see the black big-cat turn away with a female mallard in its jaws, to lope through a stand of hazel and disappear into dense fern cover.

Jimmy decided not to wait a moment longer. To get out of the woods into the sunlit field was all. He rose, lurching momentarily to get his balance and stumbled down to the weir pool. The fox lay dead, a terrible gash along its stomach and flank, it's hind legs dangling in the water where a male mallard also floated, dead. The other mallard had gone.

Dazed, Jimmy walked into the field. "Stritt". The dipper sped by him following the stream. He saw the young couple standing watching him.

"What was all that noise mate?" the young man asked.

"Oh, a fox chasing ducks. What a racket." And he walked on keeping in the sunshine.

22

Summer Days

MERLIN awoke to the lusty calling of a male cuckoo perched in a hawthorn over the weir pool. With each almost bell like call, hawthorn blossom, the May, drifted down to land without the slightest splash or ripple on the water surface. There, joining other petals, the pink-white raft drifted slowly to the weir edge, to suddenly dart over and down into the swifter flowing stream, mother of the leat that fed the once busy mills along this waterway.

The male cuckoo called to alert his mate he was up and about, seeking the nests of dunnocks along the valley. They were "dunnock" cuckoos, in that they preferred dunnocks as the host species for their young, the female laying blue eggs, larger but similar in colour to those of the dunnocks themselves. Later in the day when a few nests had been found the male would perch nearby, then call his mate to them whereupon she would toss one egg to the ground, replacing it with one of her own and fool the nest owners.

Merlin sniffed the air, smelling the tangle of scents of hawthorn and wild cherry blossom mingling with that of wild apple from the old orchard over the stream. The big cat dropped his chin back onto the cushion of bluebells, liking their coolness.

A large buff tailed bumble bee buzzed low over the tops of bluebells, landing on Merlin's nose, to be snorted furiously away as the black leopard rose at the sound of human voices.

The buff-tailed bumble bee, the largest of its kind in the country, flew low along its circuit of "buzzing spots". It was a male and he patrolled his area, leaving his scent to attract females. He was part of a colony of a hundred bees of his kind living in the earth bank surrounding the woods. Inside the nest the queen makes wax cells in which to lay her eggs, and stores honey for the larvae as they grow.

Across the stream at the far side of the field two men and a dog stood in the shadow of a large horse chestnut tree. A low, deep growl issued from Merlin's chest and throat as if to send an unheard warning to the three intruders in his domain.

The two men chatted unaware of the cat some three hundred man paces away but the dog, a collie of eight years, rose and gazed towards the woods and he, too, growled deep in his throat.

"Stay boy, quiet now", the older of the two men said, as the younger, a man in his twenties, drew a leash hanging from his belt, and fixed it to the dog's collar.

Swallows and martins were winging in, flying low over the field, filled with the joy of homecoming as they took insects from sunlit air warming the meadow grasses. Some would move on along the valley, a few would remain to nest in familiar barns and sheds they had used the previous summer.

"I'm quite sure those are big-cat footprints", the older man said to his companion. He was pointing to spoor left by Merlin as he drank at the spot the previous night. The prints were clear and carried no claw marks.

"I'll photograph them then", the younger man said. "I'll put this coin by them for scale."

"Yes. Pity we haven't got some Plaster of Paris but never mind. We can keep an eye on the area just for our own benefit. Get a few shots could you. And then we'll obliterate them in case someone recognises them and doesn't like big-cats. I'll wager it is up there in those woods watching us right now."

"Maybe Willow senses it, or smelt a scent here. That is why he growled." The younger man knelt and took half a dozen photographs of the footprints. "There, that ought to do it. Useful for the files." He rose and stepped onto the spoor, leaving his own boot-print instead. "What do you reckon? Shall we go over into the woods or leave it today?"

The older man stared longingly at the long broadleaved wood on the hillside. It was more his domain for he'd grown up here from early boyhood and few others could say they'd been here man and boy for nigh on fifty years. He knew every nook and cranny, each bend in path and stream, every hedgerow den, the buzzard nests and woodpecker holes, every tree.

"I guess we could follow the stream today son. If the cat's over there it'll want some peace wouldn't you say."

"Yes. Let's go check out the dippers. The sun is right for some nice pictures where they perch on the jutting stones. Anyway we don't want Willow stressed out."

"Agreed. And I know the moorhens have young now, up on the bend where this field joins the next. We may get a picture or two of them. The adults are excellent parents and what always gets me is that when the young have grown, if their mother has a second brood on the go the first lot of young will help with the raising of the new chicks. I believe they are the only British birds to do that. Quite remarkable."

The trio strolled downstream watched by Merlin who now sat on his haunches, relaxed and at ease.

A brown trout leapt and splashed back into the weir pool, ripples forming a widening circle of floating hawthorn blossom and sending moving lights onto the earth bank and old stonework of the weir and a small, single-arched bridge.

23

Scrumpers All

A DROUGHT had been upon the whole country for several weeks and moles were seen above ground hunting for alternative prey to earthworms who had been driven down deep into the soil by arid conditions at the surface. Even foxes and badgers were about at all hours for they, too, are great earthworm hunters forced to compensate for night-time lean pickings.

Merlin found the dry conditions and heat a strain in that he laid up by day and only ventured forth at night when the air cooled. His lair at this time was an old ochre mine, a cool "digging" beneath rock in a wooded hillside within a shrub screened quarry.

White admirals, wood whites and black hairstreak butterflies reappeared in old haunts, proving to local naturalists that climate had played its role in their distribution every bit as much as changing agricultural practices.

A long spell of warm easterlies brought Camberwell Beauties to our shores and ladybirds were in such abundance as to be labelled "in pest proportions" by miserable humans who would grumble and moan whatever the weather.

Beech and birch trees suffered sunburn, dropping their leaves prematurely, as farmers suffered their own hardships though the people of the land fared as well as ever other than having water restrictions placed upon them.

Merlin hunted at night. He flourished on rabbits, deer and smaller mammals, drinking copiously from streams that still ran sweet with fresh water, though shallow and much narrower than usual, and fields turned brown instead of green across the landscape. For the leopard it was a peaceful time in that the countryside became quiet in farming areas as more and more people went to the English beaches day after day, revelling in burning their skins off.

Stable high pressure systems persisted as a blocking anti-cyclone diverted depressions southwards into the Mediterranean regions and they suffered the wet summers Britain often found all too familiar.

Merlin's head pressed more heavily into the bluebells and he slept into the day as a pair of willow warblers moved about in the tree canopy, the male singing his mellow, descending trill as the female built a nest close to the ground by a deer track. Occasionally the cat opened one eye to watch the little olive coloured bird's busy movements but he did not eat willow warblers and paid her no real heed. All about was the movement of birds busily nesting or feeding young, and of bees busy about the business of pollen gathering.

Through narrowed eyes he watched a stoat pass across his vision, head down, intent upon some prey scent along a track barely discernible through the drifts of May-time blue-bells. The small, lithe carnivore passed by unaware of the leopard, nasally focussed on hoped for prey for he could smell rabbit and he was hungry.

Merlin half dozed. He could hear the stoat moving away but moments later the thumping of a rabbit had him awake and fully alert. He sat up again, black and hidden in the tree shadows, to see a large, plump rabbit bounding towards him, eyes rolling in terror. The animal ran to within a foot of the big cat, suddenly seeing the dark bulk of the cat and halting, dread in his stocky grey-brown furred body.

Merlin swatted the rabbit on the head with his right forepaw and the animal died instantly just as the stoat reap-peared following its scent line. Merlin watched, his great paw still resting on the dead rabbit, as the stoat rose on his haunches, swore, chattering angrily at the cat, then turning it went off to seek another meal, leaving the big-cat to the spoils that were rightfully his.

Merlin often roamed far afield at night, crossing fields and lanes, roaming woods, dusty still even into the night but always there was food for the predators, perhaps even moreso as plump rabbits, pheasants and such lay heat stricken by the drought and barely moved to escape their doom as leopard, puma, fox, stoat and weasel hunted the nights.

Then in the last days of August the drought broke dramatically with heavy rain. Dust became immediate mud as water fell in vertical sheets. Streams and rivers became full, from source to estuary as the autumn run of salmon, lying about the sea coast waiting for the scent of the rivers of their birth, swept upstream leaping weirs and waterfalls to reach gravely redds to spawn.

So Merlin feasted on salmon. His first catch was a large ten pound fish held in a shallow pool at moonlight. He was lapping water, thirsty following the last hot day when the great fish appeared shining and vibrant before him. It was a matter of moments, the swiping of one clawed forepaw, and the fish was writhing on the bank just as a goldfish might be extracted from a garden pool by a domestic cat. A bite behind the head and the flapping was stilled, the salmon dying in the waters of its birth just below the redd where its mother had laid over ten thousand eggs. It had lived here as parr and smolt, migrating to sea to feed and grow along the coasts of Europe, into the Norwegian Sea and off Greenland for over three years.

Merlin licked his fish scaled lips, liking the new taste of succulent flesh. He ate his fill and leaving the remains by the poolside he drank deeply as torrential rain fell yet again to further swell rivers and streams.

For three days it rained, water rising to overspill into fields and lanes. Rivulets ran down the wood slopes piling soil in strange patterns about clumps of woodrush and three cornered leek.

Merlin lay watching and sleeping in the loft of the old stone barn by an orchard of plums and apples waiting to be picked. Occasionally the thud of an apple falling to the ground made him alert and he would watch the doorway with fangs bared. No-one came on the three days of almost solid rain and then with a suddenness typical of late summer into autumn, the rain ceased as bright sunshine filled the valley.

On the second day of sunshine Merlin lay sprawled in old hay in the loft. He had eaten sparsely, not liking the flooded fields and mud which was just beginning to dry up. Fortunately rats and mice had visited the barn and some had died, to be eaten swiftly between bouts of sleep and periods of watchfulness.

Now as the sun rose high at noon time the leopard groaned a deep sigh as busily chattering voices came to his forward pricked ears. He moved back into the darkest corner of the timber beamed loft where a single sunbeam, shining through a gap left by a loose roof tile, showed slowly swirling dust and tiny insects.

"There's nobody in here. I told you it wasn't used. It'll make a smashing den for our gang."

The voice came from a small, grubby boy of ten, one of three youngsters who now filled the open doorway as they gazed about.

"Coo, yes. Speshully when it's raining Jamie. You were right, wasn't he Darren? Zackly the place for our gang den."

The boy called Jamie was pleased. "Come and sit down. Let's see what we've all got for our picnic. What about you Harry?"

The boys sat on an old trestle type seat against one wall, with a view through the doorway and only window.

"I've got sandwiches and crisps. Mum did bacon, what ev you got?"

"I've got bread and cheese, and 3 apples" Jamie said. "What you got Darren?"

"Bottle of orange squash and 6 jam tarts. I reckon we are OK and mum knows we are doing this seeing it's the school holidays. Better to come out here daytimes and muck about on the computer night times." Darren arranged his "tack" neatly on a rickety table, first wiping it relatively clean with the sleeve of his jumper.

The three boys set their table carefully.

"Two bacon sandwiches, two bread and cheese, two jam tarts, an apple each and a bag of crisps each. Oh, and an orange drink. Coo, that's pretty cool I reckon. What'll we do now?" Jamie was eager to get out.

"Well, the orchard's my uncle and aunty's. I vote we go and fill up these bags with apples and take em home to our mums. Uncle said they usually fall on the floor and birds and wasps eat em, so we can go in when we like." Harry was proud he had permission to visit the orchard.

"Then I vote the same", Darren said. "Then we'll come back for our feast and decide what to do tomorrow. I like it here anyway, it's a good gang den. I wonder what's up there?"

He pointed to the loft which lay in dark shadow save for one shaft of sunlight.

"Dunno", said Harry. "I spect lots of muck. P'raps owls live up there sometimes. We can have a look sometime and store things there but let's go scrumping apples."

"It isn't scrumping if you're allowed to have em. But if nobody knows we are here it could be half scrumping I s'pose." Jamie ran out into the sunshine followed by the others.

Above in the loft Merlin yawned and rose to his feet. He had not felt threatened by the children's voices but the scent of bacon assailed his nostrils. He looked down into the barn, sniffing and saw the food laid out.

Leaping to the floor Merlin ate the bacon sandwiches then the cheese sandwiches. He sniffed at the apples, his nudging nose knocking them rolling across the floor and then he licked at and ate the jam tarts. The crisps, in bags, he could not eat, and feeling the warm sunshine bathing the floor through the doorway he wandered outside. He could hear the children's voices over the hedge so he went on along the hedgerow and up into the woods to the old foxes earth at the wood top. The earth fall had left a large dry cavern which had mossed over and here Merlin stretched out in comfort to watch the woods.

In the orchard Jamie shouted to his two half-scrumper

companions that it must be time to go back to their new den to eat.

"Come on!" he shouted. "We've got enough apples. Let's go and eat."

Two minutes later the three gaped in disbelief at their bags of crisps and bottle of orange juice.

"Look, there's the apples against the wall. What rotter has been here scoffing our food? Must have been some other gang." Harry was shaking his fists furiously.

"Well why didn't they eat, or take our crisps and drink then. And the apples? Everyone likes crisps." Darren looked puzzled.

"Funny sort of gang, only sandwich eaters. Oh and our jam tarts are all gone. And where did they go? We should have seen or heard them. I reckon there must be at least three to eat all that lot chaps. Shall we search for them?"

Jamie looked crestfallen. "No I don't reckon it will do any good. Sides, they may be a lot older than us. Whoever it is knows it's a den now."

Harry was thoughtful.

"P'raps it was an animal that likes sandwiches. Yes that's it. A farm dog. Uncle's got two collies who'll eat anything. I bet they are out around the farm doing their job. That's it, dogs. They left the apples. Dogs don't eat apples. And they can't open crisp bags." Harry looked triumphant.

The others stared at him.

"Well", Jamie said. "I'm not feedin' your uncle's dogs. We'll keep the den as it's good but I'm bringing food in my satchel and next time I'm storing it on that nail in the wall, up out of the way of your uncle's dogs."

"I agree", said Harry. "Let's go home and come again tomorrow. We'll say we had a good time."

"We did have a good time", Darren said. "And I vote we stay in our den as much as we can. It's a good place."

The three boys wandered homewards chatting about the morrow and how to safeguard food from farm dogs.

24

An Urban Jaunt

MISTY rain on a chill night following a pink clouded sunset. The long, straight, steeply sloping street glistened, the pavements bright with reflected light from windows and street lighting. At 7pm it was dark, Britain's "daylight saving" clock changes but a few days past in late October.

Merlin sat in the dark shadows of a cobbled archway which led from a church, out to the street and the urban world of humans. He had left the wooded valley he had lived in for a few weeks to lope up along a tree lined lane, an old packhorse route now popular with dog walkers and nature watchers.

Passing traffic had deterred him from moving on for a while, the hiss, hiss, hiss of vehicle tyres on wet tarmac, and sweeping beams of headlights human things to avoid. Then all became quieter, the stream of people on wheels heading away from their employment and home to meals and TV screens ceasing for the night. Merlin rose from his shelter beneath a dense holly tree, itself sheltered by Scots pines, and he plodded along the now peaceful roadside.

He did not know that the Scots pine trees had had two ospreys arrive in their topmost branches a few days before and now they perched night-roosting over him, eyes closed but ears hearing his padded footfalls on autumn leaves. They had flown south, very late, from the Scottish Highlands where they had raised two young, and were now on their way following the sun to Africa, home of Merlin's own ancestors. By day the ospreys fed on fish caught in rivers, lakes and reservoirs en route. Here in the Westcountry food was plentiful and the two fish hawks were fattening up well for their journeying, entertaining the farming landowner and his family mean while.

Merlin drew into the roadside as yet another vehicle passed by spraying him with water from puddles in its passing. He shook himself and broke into a loping trot having turned right along a lesser road with bungalows set back in long gardens on one side and tall trees shedding autumn leaves on the other. He was bemused, the suddenness of houses and vehicles thrusting upon him from the seclusion and peace of the wooded valley and farm lane too much, and he loped on by them to enter a darker side road with a single iron bollard at its entrance to prevent vehicle access. Here Merlin passed, lifting his tail to spray the obstruction with his urine, scent marking his presence. Then on he went down a steep incline between high rock cliffs covered in vegetation and topped with trees, coming to another roadway with a narrow tarmac covered lane leading off it.

Merlin followed this between high brick walls, coming to steps shining wetly beneath a single street lamp. Bounding up these he passed high railings behind which stood a Norman church and churchyard with many gravestones. His feet padded on cobblestones laid a century before and a tawny owl hooted as he passed ivy clad walls with maidenhair and hartstongue ferns growing from stone crevices.

A woman hurriedly putting Guinness bottles into a recycling, green plastic bin barely gave him a glance in the darkness, her spectacles misted by the drifting rain.

"Hello boy. Where's your owner then?" A masculine voice from the first doorway of two beneath the archway had Merlin pause. A friendly human voice. Dimming memories stirred, the cat seeing again in his mind's eye the bearded face of his old friend, his former owner, whom he loved in the way cats may love a human.

"You shouldn't be out on your own in this weather boy. Or is it girl? Let's hope your owner isn't far behind."

Merlin sat on his haunches. The man, parish clerk to the local parish council unlocked the heavy black oak door with a huge key, pushing it open on creaking iron hinges. He was first "on duty" as usual. Open up, have the Minutes book and correspondence ready for the five parish councillors to make their thoughts and deliberations known. He shivered in the cold. Better light the fire, well, switch it on, cheer the wet night.

He looked at the dog, as he thought it was in the almost darkness. Black Labrador probably, popular breed, quiet sort of animal just sitting there out of the rain. Funny shaped head, and what a tail. He suddenly became conscious of the long curved tail. Odd that. Oh well, must get on before the Chairman arrives. He groaned inwardly. He'll prattle on as usual, loves the sound of his own voice. Nice chap though, pedantic, knows it all, makes the simple task a heavy one. He glanced again at Merlin's still, black shape, shrugged his shoulders and clambered noisily up the ancient wooden stairs to the little room over the arch with its plain leaded light windows overlooking the long street.

Yes there's the chairman walking jauntily across the road to the archway, and there's the vice chairman's car pulling in to the kerb. He grinned. They're arriving in order of rank, he thought, chuckling to himself. Chairman a retired schoolmaster, vice chair a real farmer, and the others, a farmer's wife, a livestock food rep' and an ex RAF officer living in the parish.

Merlin sat quietly watching the street. He was tired and wet.

A short, stocky man walked towards him, clicked his tongue in friendly manner and went by to enter the stairway and clatter briskly up it. Then another, a tall man, strode by talking to a woman and they too went upstairs, followed swiftly by two other men. The parish council had a full quorum.

"Is that loose dog still down in the arch?" the clerk asked.

"Yes, tis." The farmer, who'd arrived with his farmer's wife aunt, answered. "Didn't recognise it but there are always new people and new dogs about. For a second there I thought twas one of those big-cats people are seeing. Very long tail. But I was in my sheep skin jacket and it didn't attack me."

He laughed at the others' faces. "I haven't lost any live-stock have you auntie?"

"No. I do know that many sightings are genuine though", she replied.

"Hrmm, hrmm. Good evening all. Let's get the meeting underway shall we. And no Beast of Exmoor items on the agenda I hope. Minutes of the last meeting I believe Philip", the chairman said to the clerk.

Half way down on the left side of the street light spilled onto the wet paving slabs as a young couple left the Fish & Chip shop with fish, chips and peas clutched in eager hands.

"Let's walk home by the church for a change Sue, I've been looking forward to this supper. Mmmm, lovely chips." The young man glanced at his wife.

"OK. Suits me love. It'll be more sheltered through the arch and up round the churchyard and old school. Yes, nice chips."

They walked up the street in silence, crossing the road to the dark, looming archway.

Merlin watched their approach, smelling the food's aroma and he felt his hunger as a sudden pang of hollowness in his lean frame and stomach.

"Oh, a dog sat there look. A black retriever I think. Here dog, have a chip."

The woman held out a large chip, seeing the huge fangs flash white as the tit-bit was taken. Her husband followed suit, offering Merlin a chip which he took silently, then reaching out with a forepaw he knocked the remainder of the fish and chips from the man's hand and began to eat.

"Bloody hell, that's not a dog! Here Sue, throw it your fish and chips too and let's get out of here. That is one of them big cats that was on the TV news. Give me that and scoot."

He grabbed the food from his startled wife's hands, dropped it in front of Merlin's busy face, grabbed his wife's arm and walked very quickly away with her back down the lamp-lit street to the local pub.

"In here. Lots of light and people. Two whiskies please landlord. Hell's bells, all our fish and chips too." He laughed nervously. "Let's not say a word to anyone Sue, they'll only laugh at us."

In the dimly lit archway Merlin had eaten the two pieces of fish and all the chips. He shook himself and stretched. Walking to the second door under the arch he rose on his hind legs, digging his claws into the oak panels, raking downwards as he stretched again in the manner of all cats the world over. Knocking the heavy iron door knocker as he did so.

Then came the loud clamour of church bells pealing, telling all for a mile or more around that it was Tuesday, bell practice night. At the sound Merlin loped off back the way he had come, down the steep flight of stone steps to veer right along a narrow drangway between an old factory and the former school's boundary wall. Here he brushed by a courting couple busy in the dark shelter of a doorway that once led into the church "morgue", or "place of rest", for the dearly departed.

"Oh don't push so hard", the young woman giggled.

"Twas a dog did it, not me. Well, you know what I mean."

Merlin loped on. Beneath the arch, the woman who had answered the knock on the almshouse door stared at new scratchmarks in disbelief.

"Blimmin vandals Fred", she called. "They not only knocked the door and ran away, they scratched the wood as well. They'll be well away by now I 'spect."

She went back inside slamming the door to.

Truer words were never spoke. Merlin "the vandal" was well away. Along the dark lane he loped, passing the bollard he had sprayed earlier, running on along the roadside as vehicle lights came brighter and closer from behind him, the van slowing to keep pace just behind his tail end.

Inside the vehicle a man watched the big-cat excitedly. He knew immediately he was watching a black leopard running loose in the countryside.

He drove slowly and carefully, admiring the lithe, rippling, muscular gait of the cat in his headlights, accentuated by the wet pelage in the misty rain. He knew, too, who he should phone about the sighting, not the police but an old acquaintance, Jack Wakeley, who he was sure used to have such an animal.

Merlin ran on, turning left at the road end then on for a hundred yards to run left again into the lane leading to his valley home, and was gone into the darkness.

25

Another of His Kind

MERLIN was hungry. He had lain most of the day basking in sunshine on a mound of grassed over soil that had once been the earth of a hedge bank across the field. The landowner had obtained a grant to remove the hedge, making one large field of two smaller ones. Merlin liked the vantage point, using it for over a week of fine weather with clear nights and a moon coming to the full.

With nightfall the field and woods had lost their constant bird song and the bees had gone to rest. Merlin watched a fox cross the field, keeping within the shadow of the hedge. He knew its earth deep in the woods, close by a sett of badgers but he rarely went near, preferring to keep to the track through the woods made by deer.

Along this well used animal trail he often found food, creeping up then rushing his quarry, usually a rabbit or pheasant. Sometimes he lay across a huge beech tree branch, to drop on roe or red deer, killing swiftly with the ease of a leopard in its prime.

Now he rose and stretched, moving silently to the nearest oak tree. Raising himself up on his hind legs he unsheathed his claws into the bark and stretched again, tearing scratch marks into the tree in the way of all cats and feeling every muscle tighten with power as he did so.

Head and body, Merlin was now over one and a half metres in length, with a tail almost a metre long. Over two foot at the shoulders and weighing a hundred pounds he was the perfect feline carnivore. When rushing large prey he was capable of a speed of 60km per hour and a final leap of five or six metres, killing by a bite at the throat or the nape of the neck.

He ate by tearing the viscera of his prey first, usually at

the abdomen and then into the chest cavity, relishing the main body organs, especially of roe and red deer. His mouth watering at the thought of food to come he loped to a favourite gap in the hedge and into the wood where he had cached the remains of a recent kill, a roe deer doe.

Merlin had killed the deer the previous day's morning, rushing a family group of these browsing a bramble brake at first light. He dragged the carcase from the steep field into the wood edge and had gorged until sated. At such times with an abundance of prey about he rarely travelled far afield, preferring to remain in an area he knew well if it was relatively undisturbed by man and dog.

Now he moved lithely to where the carcase was hid in dense undergrowth, to find it untouched by scavengers. Often he had tended to cache prey in a tree but the main scavengers, foxes and brown rats avoided his scent marking when they came upon it. Merlin had never tasted fox meat, ignoring them in the main, and rats he killed and ate so they were not as numerous about the farmstead as they once were.

Merlin ate his fill and leaving the remains where they lay he moved down over the slope to the stream, drinking deeply. Washing his wet face using tongue and forepaw he cleaned the dead deer smell from his fur, then sat watching the valley from half way up the hillslope.

Two fields away a small herd of red deer grazed peacefully, clearly visible in the moonlight. Beyond them was a farmhouse with one lighted window, backed by a long forestry plantation of thousands of conifers grown as a crop.

Merlin watched the deer absently. Occasionally the breeze carried their scent to him but he was not hungry and hunted only for food. Then another scent reached him and Merlin bared his fangs in a silent snarl. It was the scent of leopard, a scent like his own and the big-cat lowered his lean body into the high grass where earlier in the day marbled white and meadow brown butterflies had fluttered in the sunshine.

He saw all the deer suddenly raise their heads in unison, to scatter and run as a black shadow of a shape detached itself from the forest to rush amongst them. Merlin saw the charge and leap, saw the big-cat bring down the nearest deer to it as the herd gathered together to leap a gate one by one, into a lane leading to the farm. He watched as the black shape dragged the deer into a scrub spinney at the field corner and he knew that a cat like himself was feeding. Instinctively he wanted to go to the other cat but he remained still, knowing when he himself was hungry and feeding he tolerated no disturbance. He watched on for an hour but saw no further movement from the spinney, nor did he see the cat go silently back into the forest the way she had come.

Merlin arose and turned away, wandering back to his lair without a backward glance...

26

Winter

A WESTCOUNTRY winter holds no hardships for cats such as Merlin. Though his kind were indigenous to countries with hotter climes, nights were often very cold, much colder at times than an English winter.

In the past Merlin had passed several weeks in the Bradiford Valley of his early days with Jack Wakely, moving occasionally out along the Pudnor Woods area and Blakewell Mill where he had been sighted a few times. Once he had been shot at by a farmer who'd missed and chuckled as the cat charged away, to come to Broomhill and Muddiford with its forestry and streams. The cat marked his territory in these places, returning to the Bradiford Valley frequently, thus establishing a large territory as his own, revisiting the whole every three or four weeks.

And now it was winter. On one starlit night when Sirius was high and sparkling as brightly as the frost laden grasses he had watched two foxes meet and mate near a wood edge, hearing their screaming barks and seeing them run up over the hill into the woods where the dog fox had his earth, or den. Merlin did not concern himself with foxes other than as competition for the same smaller food, though he occasionally killed deer, which foxes could not.

Now he lay, head on forepaws in his favourite hedgebank lair, listening to the soft patter of snow falling upon the land as an east wind moaned in leafless trees above him. Merlin did not know snow and earlier had puzzled and pawed at the hardness of the water where he usually drank by the weir. His pawing had broken the ice formed over the weir pool. He had drunk his first icy cold water then, quenching his thirst even as the water surface began to freeze over once more, so cold was the air all about. He saw Sirius sparkling in the pool before his eyes and tried to nose and paw at its reflection, feeling some strange bond with the star millions of light years away, but it shimmered and dulled with the thickening of the ice and falling flakes of snow, then was gone.

Merlin had then plodded up into the woods, rushing onto a fat rabbit nibbling at grass by a narrow path and, missing, ran headlong into a male pheasant about to fly up into the trees. His meal secure for the day he wandered up along his own pathway to his lair at the western top corner of the woods.

Come morning he awoke to a strange light before his eyes, a hitherto unknown paleness and his questing nose found a soft coldness, alien to him. Merlin pushed harder with his nose, finding himself gazing down over a white woodscape as the curtain of snow blocking his exit fell away. He rose, reaching his forepaws out from the snug lair and digging his claws into the snowy soil he stretched then stepped from the hideout.

All about him was whiteness with stalks of grasses and other dead vegetation starkly protruding and here and there clumps of green moss showing through, growing on long dead tree stumps. He started as a shower of snow fell upon him from a branch on which a crow as black as he had just alighted. Merlin snarled up at the crow but the large black bird crawed loudly at him from its swaying perch then flew low through the trees seeking food.

Merlin had taken to hunting mainly by day, using the dusk and dawn as his favoured times, finding prey easier to come by and the countryside less pestered by humans. Now he padded silently down over the wood slope, feeling the cold wetness on his paws and upon his head, shoulders and back as he pushed past familiar shrubs, seeing his exhaled breaths upon the cold air before him.

He paused at the stile above the weir, watching for any movement, sniffing at badger hair caught on wire, then he pushed through a gap at the side of the stile to arrive above

All about him was whiteness.

the weir. Here the Bradiford Water, joined a field away, upstream, by the Colam Stream, rushed over, swollen by recent rains and melt- water. Merlin watched leaves and small branches rushing over the weir, building up into a trash dam where alder roots reached to hold them fast. A Kingfisher alighted by him then with a whirr of blue, chestnut and white, flew to the weir pool to seek a meal. The bird was one of a pair that nested in the bank of the old mill leat where elm tree stumps in a row held the bank and told of Dutch Elm disease that had killed many thousands of elm trees across the countryside.

Merlin moved away from the weir. Its loud roaring sound of rushing water bothered him for he could not hear other sounds and needed to do so for the easier catching of food, and for his own safety. He trotted between two oaks and out onto a meadow which led to others along the valley. Here a flock of redwings, some sixty or so, put up from the grass to chitter along a hawthorn hedge, eating crimson berries as they did so. The redwings, a species of thrush had flown from harder climes in Scandinavia seeking food as had hundreds of fieldfares, larger, grey thrushes. A flock of over one hundred of these were busy feeding on seeds beneath a row of small trees the snow had not penetrated. At Merlin's arrival amongst them they rose vertically as one, to fly chattering into the next field.

A pair of magpies harassed him, one flying low over his head but Merlin's swift retaliation, an upwards sweeping forepaw lost the bird a tail feather and the two retreated noisily to the woods.

Now Merlin was in a field by a former mill and suddenly he paused as movement near a fence caught his attention. A group of roe deer were feeding close to three cock and six hen pheasants and beyond them a man was walking away with an empty sack. The man occasionally threw out food in winter for the animals so that his two children could watch them with their mother from the cosy lounge on the second floor of the old mill. Now he jerked around suddenly as the sound of coughing roars reach his ears and he saw one deer fall to the ground, a large black cat tearing its throat as it fell.

"Hells Bells!" the man shouted, then turned and ran for home, slamming and bolting the mill door in one movement. "Look!" he called to his wife, "get to the window quick!"

But Merlin was already half way across the field heading back to the woods, carrying his prey, head high, the legs of the deer dragging a wide and bloody track in the snow.

"Dad, we could track it and find out where it goes", shouted the eldest of the two children.

"No way", their father replied, "the cat is to be left alone. And don't you dare go looking for it, that's an order. Keep in this garden until I say. This is our big secret mind, no telling anyone at all or the poor old cat'll be shot."

"We wont tell", chorused the two boys.

Merlin paused to drop his prey by the leat pool where he drank deeply, then getting a better grip on the small deer he moved lithely up over the woods to his lair and feasted. Then dragging the remains of the carcase to the top of the bank above his lair he released it to roll into dense brambles, hidden from view. He felt a flurry of snow on his face and curling up contentedly in the earth cavern he slept.

For just three days it snowed spasmodically with intermittent rain, only the high ground of Dartmoor, Exmoor and Bodmin in the Westcountry having minor problems with drifting and any noticeable depth to the snow. The snowplough owned by the Highways Authority had not been used for twenty years and people talked of global warming, prophesying great storms and much flooding in the near future.

The tracks from mill to woodlands had disappeared under snow during the night of the kill, the roe deer now living in the extensive grounds of a large house nearby. The family living in the converted mill had kept their secret though the two boys played Tarzan games in the large rambling rooms of their home or watched the fields with the family binoculars.

But Merlin did not return to the mill but hunted further afield, deeper into farming country where food was plentiful as the weather gradually improved.

27

A Mate

"HOH-OO, hoh-oo". The late spring calling of a male long-eared owl carried on the night air from the large, dark forestry plantation on the hillside across the valley from Merlin's lair. The somewhat mournful sound was not unlike that made when someone blows closely across the top of an empty drinks bottle.

"Hoh-oo". The low pitched, two tone call came again as the long-ear assured his mate all was well in the forest and the five dull white eggs she had laid on the flattened roof of a squirrel's drey would not be harmed.

The male owl flew to the nest tree from his favourite perch in another tree nearby, flapping his wings in the face of a black leopard about to come too close to his mate on their eggs. The leopard wavered, feeling the owls wings strike her nose and she leapt to the ground onto soft pine needles.

The owl flew back to his perch. Soon he would hunt small rodents to bring to his mate and when the young hatch he would hunt for them also while his mate feeds them. For two months the long-ear would be busy, resting and watching by day, hunting and feeding by night.

"Hoh-oo". He fluffed his feathers then flew after the leopard to see if she disturbed out any small prey in her passing. He was smaller and slenderer than a tawny owl, with glowing orange eyes and ear tufts he sometimes held raised.

Across the valley Merlin eyed the deer in the field he had seen one of his kind make a kill. Two weeks had passed since then and he had visited outlying areas of his territory, marking known spots to let others know of his presence. At

The owl flew back to his perch.

two locations he had at last found the scent marking of the female at points where their territories overlapped slightly. It was the first sighting he had had of another leopard other than that of his mother and another cub when he was born and Merlin was excited.

Merlin came again to the female leopard's marking spot at a broken wall where erosion and accretion of a bend in the stream bank formed a small "beach" and deep pool from which to drink, used by many animals. He sniffed the female's mark and sprayed beside it on fallen stones as he'd done for many weeks. Thus did Merlin know the female was newer to the area than he and that she must be aware of his presence in the vicinity, from his marking.

He crossed the waterway, swimming briefly in the pool, enjoying the feel of cold water and drinking as he did so. Hauling himself onto the bank he shook his pelage free of water, then rolled in the high grasses to further dry himself.

Suddenly deer passed him at a trot, swerving away on sighting him, eyes rolling, bewildered, for moments before they had seen the black leopard enter the field behind them. But it was not Merlin they had seen and as he charged and leapt for the neck of the nearest, so another was tripped and killed by the hunting female.

The remainder of the deer splashed in panic across the waterway, to huddle in the darkness of the woods knowing the chase, such as it was, was over.

Merlin stood beside his kill, looking across the field to the female standing by hers. She left the carcase and trotted towards him making curious grunting sounds as he padded towards her. When they were but a leopard's pace apart she turned sideways to him snarling silently, white fangs gleaming in the moonlight.

Merlin could smell deer blood on them both but he could smell the female and his own blood pounded within him as primeval instincts brought his maleness above all else. Growling he mounted her, finding her receptive and biting into her neck he held her to him as she snarled and growled aloud with their mating.

When they broke apart the female turned on him with
bites and snarls and hungry now Merlin trotted back to his
prey and his mate to hers. Then, suddenly he found her
beside him, touching flank to flank and they both ate
ravenously from his kill.

Hunger satisfied the two leopards dragged both carcases
into hiding, then drank from the stream pool where brown
trout watched their moonlit silhouettes and the momentary
clouding of the water as blood from their meal washed from
fur and whiskers.

Merlin crossed the stream by shallows further along the
bank, the female following him into the woods and into a
crevice formed by rock falls centuries before. Squeezing
through the narrow opening behind her mate she found
herself in a large cave, invisible from without, unknown
even to the landowner who rarely visited this part of the
woods.

Merlin lay down with a noisy grunt. Turning thrice about
the female lay beside him and they slept.

28

Epilogue

JACK Wakely grinned. Two years had passed since he'd driven a black leopard called Merlin to free him at Wistlandpound Reservoir. Every day since then he had wondered about his feline friend, often with pangs of remorse and just as often with a lump in his throat.

Stories and reports of black big-cats and pumas on the loose in the wild had naturally increased as interest in the animals grew. He had based his decision to set Merlin free on knowing how extremely elusive all cats can be, and that Merlin would not attack humans unless attacked first.

Jack had pushed on with his own loner life, knowing full well that some of the eye witness reports were probably of Merlin but there was no way of really being certain though he plotted all sightings that came his way onto a map of the region.

On the morning of the day after Merlin had been about Pilton Church archway eating fish and chips, Jack had been visited by Dick Norman. Dick it was who had seen the big-cat from his vehicle and followed it to a local lane entrance into a wooded valley. The two men had chatted about the incident and Jack felt sure Merlin "was back", for he and the cat had lived together less than a mile from Dick's sighting.

Now he stood on Beer's Bridge, a stoutly built wooden bridge over a waterway that once turned seven mill wheels along its route, and was the home of otters, kingfishers and brown trout. He had stood thus every evening for three weeks, nodding to dog walkers and chatting to birdwatchers but always scanning the hill slopes on either side of the woods he knew so well.

Then on the twenty-first day of his vigil, in the golden

From the woods came a black shape.

light of evening, his heart missed a beat as onto the west-ward hill slope from the woods came a black shape. Focussing his binoculars he could clearly see a black leopard stroll out onto the field to sit gazing back towards the woods. It was then Jack thought he was hallucinating or just thinking wishfully, for another black big-cat wandered from the woods to sit beside the first. Two black leopards. Merlin had a mate. What a turn-up.

He grinned again, pondering on risking going over to see his old friend more closely.

"Evening Mr. Wakely. Something interesting?"

He jumped. So engrossed was he in watching the cats even his keen ears had not heard the approach of the landowner.

"Oh, just looking about. Saw the dippers just now."

He noticed with alarm the farmer had a twelve-bore under his arm. The farmer chuckled.

"Did you now. Always dippers here. My father knew their every nest, and the otter holts. We had a chap build us an imitation holt once. You'll know him."

He named a local naturalist, saying the man had also had the mill leat cleared to improve the habitat for dragonflies and other water life.

"Yes. Good chap. Often see him about. Born near here wasn't he?"

"Yes. Just over the hill. Knows his stuff. Interested in all these big-cats too. Beast of Exmoor and all that stuff. I must say that any on my land are welcome to stay. I've lost no livestock. I do like a rabbit now and then. Carry my shotgun just in case. But anyone upsetting the cats on my land will be upsetting me and the missus and that wont help them one bit. Don't need people like that."

The farmer raised his hat. "Have a good evening Mr. Wakely. Go where you like as long as you don't disturb any wildlife, black, brown or any other colour."

He strode off along the streambank, humming a country song.

Jack stood watching him go. Then he turned to see the

cats stretched out together high on the hillside. He knew one was Merlin.

He waved and turned away homeward. Yes, he thought, tomorrow I'll get myself a collie from the Dog Rescue Centre. Tis time for a new pal.

29

The Leopard: Factfile

About the Leopard (Panthera pardus) Linnaeus 1758

The Leopard is a big cat. Its head and body length, for a male, attains 1.15–1.67 metres, females being 0.95–1.24 metres. The tail is 0.58–0.96 metres. Height at shoulder is 0.45–0.80 metres. Weight is 35–54kg.

A male reaches maturity at 2–3 years, females at approximately 2 years. Longevity is up to 24 years. Gestation period 93–98 days. Number of young 1–4 cubs. Weight at birth 430–00g. Weaned at about 3 months.

The normal leopard is spotted, with dark rosettes on a ground colour of straw through to deep ochre. The pelage, or coat, may be dense and short, or long and silky depending on the climate. Undersides of throat, belly and neck are white as are the centre of the back of the ears. Rosettes are often open in the centre, and spots may be seen in the tail where they become rings towards the tip.

Melanistic individuals are frequently found and referred to as "black panthers", whilst cream coloured individuals and albinos are also found. Cubs are miniatures of their parents and appear darker because the spots are closer together. The female usually has four pairs of teats.

The leopard has a wide distribution and is common in Africa South of the Sahara, and still found in the North of the continent. It is found in Asia, the Sinai Peninsula and Israel. Its range continues east to Siberia's Amur area and South to the Malayan Peninsula and Indo-China. The leopard is also present on the Northern slopes of the Caucasus mountains and is thus a European species.

Leopards are remarkably adaptable to a whole range of habitats but seem to avoid actual desert. They rarely move more than 3000 metres above sea level. The leopard is usually solitary, but not always.

Whether it is nocturnal or diurnal depends on the degree of

disturbance and level of competition so daytime sightings are not unusual, especially where it is top predator.

Males hold territories which may overlap with other males and individuals space themselves by marking and visit each part of their territory about once a month. Females also hold a territory and these may overlap with other females or be within that of a male. Leopards may travel 25 kms in a night and have been known to travel up to 75 kms.

A leopard hunts its prey by stalking until it is close then making a charge followed by a leap of up to six metres. A charge may reach 60 kms per hour. The usual method of killing is a bite at the throat or nape of the neck. Usually the cat begins eating the viscera of the prey and frequently drags the carcase into hiding before beginning to eat. When it has finished eating it caches the remainder of the carcase in a tree, or in undergrowth.

Leopards will eat mice and any animal up to about 90 kg body-weight, as well as fish.

Throughout its range there is no actual breeding season but mating is usually in the spring of the year. Cubs are born blind but fully furred, the eyes opening at 9 – 10 days old. They begin to leave the den at about 5 weeks, and the adult coat is gained at about 4 months. Cubs are weaned at about 3 months and begin independence at around 18 months to 2 years. Full adult size is reached at around 3 years.

There are many sub-species of leopard, not all of which are accepted as valid by some authorities.

AUTHOR'S NOTE

As I write this, in February 2008, Exmoor Zoological Park at South Stowford, Exmoor, has just given home to Ebony, a female black leopard.

On 22nd February I had the privilege of visiting Ebony in her new home, a truly magnificent animal of great beauty and power, and, better still, I have adopted her and look forward to visiting her in the future. A dream comes true...

Exmoor Zoo is situated on the A399 between Bratton Fleming and Blackmore Gate, a must to visit. Tel: 01598 763352, or visit www. exmoorzoo.co.uk.